DURATION AND SIMULTANEITY

The Library of Liberal Arts

OSKAR PIEST, FOUNDER

Duration and Simultaneity

WITH REFERENCE TO EINSTEIN'S THEORY

Henri Bergson

Translated by
Leon Jacobson
Professor of Art, East Carolina College

With an Introduction by
Herbert Dingle
Professor Emeritus of History and Philosophy of Science
University of London

The Library of Liberal Arts

published by

THE BOBBS-MERRILL COMPANY, INC.

A Subsidiary of Howard W. Sams & Co., Inc.

Publishers • Indianapolis • New York • Kansas City

Henri Bergson: 1859–1941
Durée et Simultanéité was originally published in 1922

COPYRIGHT © 1965
THE BOBBS-MERRILL COMPANY, INC.
Printed in the United States of America
Library of Congress Catalog Card Number 64-66064
First Printing

Translator's Preface

IT IS the moral of Bergson's philosophy that we shall not live as fully as we could, and that philosophy and science will not co-operate as they might, as long as we remain unaware that "it is time which is happening and, more than that, which causes everything to happen." If we do not notice the actuality and efficacy of time, it is not through oversight, but because time is ruled out by the intelligence, whether exercised in our daily problem-solving or, much more precisely, in scientific investigation. For our intellect was made to prepare our action upon things; and action is taken on fixed points. Our intelligence, looking for fixity, masks the flow of time by conceiving it as a juxtaposition of "instants" on a line.

But, in Bergson's view, despite this normal exteriorization of our feeling of duration into a "spatialized" time, the mind, being more than intellect, is still capable of apprehending universal becoming in a vision in which "what was immobile and frozen in our perception is warmed and set in motion." It is possible to "reascend the slope of nature" and, by a concentrated effort of attention, by "intuition," to contact directly, deep within, that concrete duration which is "the very stuff of our existence and of all things."

Bergson well understood, then, that it is our practical routine that has militated against a renewal, or deepening, of our perception; that "our senses and our consciousness have reduced real time and real change to dust in order to facilitate our action upon things." Nor, certainly, does he condemn positive science for not being concerned with duration (even though that is its inspiration), since "the function of science is, after all, to compose a world for us in which we can, for the convenience of action, ignore the effects of time." What he deplores, however, is the tendency of science, and philosophy, to mistake its conceptualizations of reality for reality itself. It is, indeed, against a biological and psychological "metaphysics" that Bergson's major works are directed, always with the ultimate aim of clearing the path to vision. *Duration and Simultaneity* is the concluding chapter in this long polemic with scientism.

In the work before us, Bergson argues against the demand by "the theoreticians of relativity," made in the name of Einstein's theory of special relativity, that we believe in the "slowing" of time by motion in each relatively moving system in the universe. Of course, the very notion of slowed times runs counter to the common-sense view of a single, universal time; and it also contradicts Bergson's allied conception of duration, central in his philosophy. It therefore becomes Bergson's purpose in *Duration and Simultaneity* to demonstrate: (1) that it is actually the supposition of multiple, real times, not that of a single, real time, which Einstein's postulate of the reciprocity of motion contradicts; (2) that the considering of Einstein's times as "real" is attributable to an oscillation, in the course of physical investigation, between the standpoints of Einstein's "bilateral" and Lorentz' "unilateral" theory of relativity; and (3) that this oscillation is itself traceable to "our not having first analyzed our representation of the time that flows, our feeling of real duration." Let us first consider this last, and widest, "frame" of Bergson's argument.

As in all his works, Bergson points out in *Duration and Simultaneity* that it is not the *experience* of duration that we ordinarily have in mind when we speak of time, but its *measurement*. For what we care about in practical life is the measurement of the real and not its nature. But we cannot directly measure that reality which is duration, since it is an indivisible flow, and therefore has no measurable parts. To be measured, it must first be spatialized. Now, the first step in this process is taken when we think of the experienced flow of our inner duration as motion in space; and the next, when we agree to consider the path described by this motion as the motion itself. In dividing and measuring the path, we then say we are dividing and measuring the duration of the motion that is tracing it.

For us, it is the earth's rotation that is the model motion tracing the path of time. Time then seems to us "like the unwinding of a thread, like the journey of the mobile [the earth] entrusted with measuring it. We shall then say that we have measured the time of this unwinding and of the universal unwinding as well." But, if we can correlate these two unwindings, it is only because we have at our disposal the concept of simultaneity; and we owe this concept to our ability to perceive external flows of events either together with the flow of our own duration, or separately from it, or, still better, both separately and together, at one and the same time. If we then refer to two external flows which take up the same duration as being "simultaneous," it is because they abide within the duration of yet a third, our own. But, to be useable, these simultaneities of durations must be converted into simultaneities of instants; and this we do as soon as we have learned to spatialize time. As noted above, we divide the path that has come to symbolize the flow of real time into equal units of space, and into "instants," which are the extremities of these units. But, now, in addition, we point off the whole length of the moving path of a contemporary event with corresponding points of division. Any portion of the duration of its motion is then considered measured when we have counted a number of such correspondences, or simultaneities.

These simultaneities are instantaneities, not partaking of the real time that endures. But they are yet simultaneous with instants pointed off by them along our inner duration, and created in the very act of pointing. Bergson declares, therefore, that it is because instant-simultaneities are imbedded in flow-simultaneities, and because the latter are referrable to our own duration, that what we are measuring is time as well as space; and, conversely, if the time being measured is not finally convertible into an experienced duration, it is not time, but space, which we are measuring.

Now, it happens that none of the motion-induced slowings of time allegedly uncovered by Einstein's theory of special relativity is convertible into duration. For, from Einstein's standpoint of the reciprocity of motion in space, these times are merely *attributed* by a real physicist-observer in a conventionally stabilized, "referrer" system S, to merely imagined physicist-observers in a conventionally mobilized, "referred-to" system S'. Not being "pasted" to a time which is either lived or livable, they are purely fictional, in no way comparable to the actually lived time of the physicist in S.

But the unreality of multiple times betokens the singleness of real time. For, were the referrer-physicist in S to betake himself to S', he would, by that very fact, be immobilizing it into a referrer system and would then live the same time there which he had lived in the former referrer system S. This interchangeability of observers and their lived times in two systems in a state of uniform and reciprocal motion is consequent upon Einstein's hypothesis of the reciprocity of motion in space. Hence, "far from ruling out the hypothesis of a single, universal duration, Einstein's theory of special relativity calls for it and confers upon it a superior intelligibility."

The fact is, according to Bergson, that it is in Lorentz' "unilateral," not Einstein's "bilateral" theory of relativity that multiple times can logically be considered real. For, it is there alone that a system of reference is regarded as at absolute rest, while other systems are in absolute motion. These conditions, found in Lorentz' theory, do imply the existence of multiple times, all on the same footing and all "real." Yet, physicists support Einstein's, not Lorentz' theory of relativity; and the question arises as to why they should attribute to Einstein a doctrine properly ascribable to Lorentz. To Bergson, this confusion of Einstein's and Lorentz' viewpoints seems almost inevitable. It stems from the fact that even when a physicist begins by granting Einstein's thesis that any two systems, S and S', are in reciprocal motion, he cannot, as a physicist, investigate this system without immobilizing one of them into a "stationary" system of reference. The result is that "absolute rest expelled by the understanding is reinstated by the imagination." In the mind of the physicist, two representations of relativity then accompany one another, one, "radical and conceptual" (Einstein's), and the other, "attenuated and imagist" (Lorentz'), and "the concept undergoes contamination by the image." In other words, even though the physicist *conceives* relativity from the standpoint of Einstein, he *sees* it a little from that of Lorentz. The multiple times—as well as the contractions in length, and dislocations of simultaneity into succession—which occur upon the application of the Lorentz transformation equations to a "moving" system, then appear real, as much in Einstein's as in Lorentz' theory of relativity.

This point is an essential part of Bergson's demonstration of the compatibility of his philosophy of duration with the considerations of time in Einstein's theory of relativity. This demonstration is, of course, Bergson's main objective in *Duration and Simultaneity*. But now, another and more general question arises as to how physicists have been led, in the first place, to embrace a paradox, namely, the existence of multiple, real times in the universe? Bergson's answer to this question inevitably brings us back to his basic philosophic theme, which consists of his distinction between real, lived time and its "spatialization" into the objects, events, and clock-time of everyday life and of scientific activity. According to Bergson, our conceptual thinking, as well as its linguistic expression, is "molded" upon a world "already made." But our intellect, in thus reflecting the world, only serves to mask reality itself, that is, the world "in the making," in short, real time or duration. Now, given the goal and method of science, physicists, at least as much as the rest of us, live in a world already made and not in the making, a world, therefore, in which what is most concrete—time and change—is only superficially experienced. "Let us become accustomed," Bergson urges, "to

see all things *sub specie durationis:* immediately in our gal-
vanized perception what is taut becomes relaxed, what is dor-
mant awakens, what is dead comes to life again." Mathematics
will not then be "given the status of a transcendent reality";
and physicists will no longer be interested in erecting Einstein's theory, just as it stands, into an unconscious metaphysics, one, moreover, that tends in the direction of an idealism based upon principles having nothing in common with
those of relativity.

As early as 1911, the thesis of the existence of multiple, real
times in Einstein's theory was dramatized in "the clock paradox of the identical twins." In that year, the eminent French
physicist Langevin stated before the International Congress
of Philosophy, meeting at Bologna, that a space-traveler will
be younger upon his return to earth than his stay-at-home
twin brother, because not only his time but also his bodily
processes will have been slowed by the vehicle's motion
through space. It was hearing this notion of "asymmetrical
aging," enunciated by Langevin, which, in fact, first drew
Bergson's attention to Einstein's theory. All of *Duration and
Simultaneity* can be considered its refutation, although the
question is directly treated only on pages 73–79, and in the
first Appendix, "The Journey in the Projectile." This Appendix is a reply to another French physicist, Becquerel, whose
position was the same as Langevin's. Bergson's last word on
the subject was contained in an article written in 1924 and
published in reply to one by André Metz, a disciple of Becquerel, in which the orthodox view was restated.

After a lapse of thirty years, the controversy over asymmetrical aging was reopened in 1956, the principal part in it being
taken, this time, by the English astrophysicist, philosopher of
science, and science educator, Herbert Dingle. The criticism
of the belief in asymmetrical aging which is advanced by
Professor Dingle rests, like that of Bergson, on the assertion

that physico-mathematical "proofs" of asymmetrical aging are vitiated by Einstein's postulate of relativity. Professor Dingle's Introduction to the present work is of great importance in itself; and it should serve to heighten the impact of Bergson's *Duration and Simultaneity* upon the intellectual world.

LEON JACOBSON

July 1965

CONTENTS

Introduction

EARLY IN this century, two very prominent, and originally independent, lines of thought collided. The area of impact included problems concerned with the experiences, or ideas, of time, simultaneity, motion. On the one hand, the chief center of interest in philosophy, it is not too much to say, was the system of Bergson, in which the *passage* of time, apprehended intuitively, was the fundamental element. On the other hand, the physical theory of relativity, which after 1919 at any rate dominated scientific thought, submerged time in a more comprehensive and essentially static "space-time," from which it could be extracted variously and largely arbitrarily by the physicist. It was inevitable that one or other of these views should give way.

As a matter of history, it was the Bergsonian movement that yielded. Its influence rapidly waned, and it was succeeded in philosophy by ideas of the logical positivist type that originated in relativity theory. But is this a final judgment? The appearance of Professor Jacobson's very clear translation of Bergson's *Durée et Simultanéité* affords an opportunity for a reconsideration of the conflict in the light of nearly half a century of subsequent research. In this necessarily too brief Introduction I shall attempt such a reassessment and try to indicate its present significance.

I should like, however, as a preliminary to reject one type of solution to the problem, to which Bergson himself, though he specifically disowns it (pp. 64–65), seems at times to resort, namely, that of postulating a fundamental distinction between philosophy and science. Originally they were one, and although, in the sense in which the words are now used, philosophers and scientists may consider different problems and approach the same problems from different directions, it is not possible that there are two equally valid solutions to the same problem. If that were so, discussion would be useless. I shall take it for granted that, on the points at issue here, Bergson and the relativists might both be wrong but cannot both be right. On that basis alone is it worth while to continue.

Let us begin with the problem which, though not the most fundamental, presents the conflict most pointedly—the problem of what has come to be known as "asymmetrical aging." This is here dealt with at length by Bergson, both in the text and in Appendix I. Paul journeys at high uniform speed to a distant star and returns two years older, according to his clock and his physical condition. Peter, however, who remains on the earth, is then some two hundred years older than when Paul left him, and has long been in his grave (p. 74). That is what, according to the great majority of its advocates, Einstein's theory of relativity requires. To Bergson, however, time lived is an absolute thing, no matter whether it is Peter or Paul who lives it. Hence, however they occupy the interval between separating and reuniting, they must live the same time and therefore age by the same amount. Therefore Bergson has to disprove the argument that leads the relativists to their conclusion.

He does this by denying that the "time" which Peter calculates that Paul's clock will record is, in fact, time. It is a "phantom," unrelated to anything that Paul experiences. In exactly the same way Paul can calculate a phantom time for Peter and thereby prove that it is Peter whose aging has been retarded. The fact that these results are contradictory proves conclusively that they cannot both be right; yet we cannot justify one without, by the same principles, justifying the other.

We can see clearly here the difference of interest that led to the contestants failing to convince one another. It was essential for Bergson to save the absolute character of time, for the intuition of time was for him of the essence of life; hence he took his stand upon that and then had to interpret the relativists' calculation, which he could not fault, as leading to a phantom time. The relativists, however, were not concerned with life. To them, Peter and Paul could have been merely names of clocks, and all that they claimed was that when the clock Paul rejoined the clock Peter, it could be observed to have recorded a shorter lapse of time. If, incidentally, there happened to be human beings standing by the clocks, they would of course age in agreement with their clock readings; and if philosophy suggested otherwise, then philosophy was wrong.

But Bergson also advanced a perfectly relevant argument even from the physical point of view. To this the relativists had no answer, and if he had allowed himself to pose as a physicist and left his philosophy out of account, he might have been able to press the point home. At the basis of the *theory* of relativity lies the *postulate* of relativity, according to which, when two (or more) bodies are in relative motion, either of them can be accorded any motion that one pleases, including none at all, provided that the other is then given whatever motion is necessary to preserve the *relative* motion. That means that no observation is possible that will enable one to say that the motion is divided between the bodies in any particular way. But if motion retards the process of aging, the relative youth of Paul on reunion would indicate that it was Paul, and not Peter, who had moved, or at least had moved more, and that would violate the postulate of relativity. Hence the theory would require that its own basis was invalid. The only possible conclusion, therefore, if the theory was not to destroy itself, was that Peter and Paul, whether men or clocks, must age at the same rate during the journey.

This consideration seems to me final. This same problem has been revived at various times since it was first conceived, and in particular, during the last nine years or so, has been the subject of vigorous controversy all over the world. With very few exceptions, physicists have maintained that the theory of relativity requires asymmetrical aging, notwithstanding the argument just given. Some years ago, in an attempt to bring the discussion to a point, I put that argument into the form of a single syllogism, in the hope that those who did not accept its conclusion would state from which of its elements they dissented, and why, and so enable agreement to be reached. Here is the syllogism, as presented in *Nature:* [1]

1. According to the postulate of relativity, if two bodies (for example, two identical clocks) separate and reunite, there is no observable phenomenon that will show in an absolute sense that one rather than the other has moved.

2. If on reunion one clock were retarded *by a quantity depending on their relative motion,* and the other not, that phenomenon would show that the first had moved and not the second.

3. Hence, if the postulate of relativity is true, the clocks must be retarded equally or not at all: in either case, their readings will agree on reunion if they agreed at separation.

Unfortunately, I underestimated the capacity of the controversialists for evading the issue. The next contribution to *Nature* [2] began, "May I suggest an alternative approach to this problem . . ."; and the writer then proceeded to a relatively involved discussion; the syllogism was not mentioned. It is hard to see why, when the problem has been reduced to the simplest possible terms, a new and indirect approach should be necessary; but, in fact, that was but one of an apparently endless succession of such approaches. I have repeated the syllogism several times, in several places, but without eliciting a single answer to the question, which of its elements is faulty, and without a single acceptance of its conclusion from any not previously convinced of it.

This is a most remarkable situation, which, quite apart from the reality or otherwise of asymmetrical aging, calls for serious inquiry. I shall revert to this later: here I shall merely try to identify its origin, which I believe lies in the history of the subject, while its endurance is facilitated by the unawareness, among the younger physicists at least, of that history. It is necessary, therefore, to recall its salient features.

1 "The 'Clock Paradox' of Relativity," *Nature,* CLXXIX (1957), 1242.
2 J. H. Fremlin, "Relativity and Space Travel," *Nature,* CLXXX (1957), 499.

From the time of Newton up to the end of the nineteenth century, mechanics was regarded as the basic science: his laws of motion and their associated equations were the foundation on which all further constructions, in the metrical sciences at least, had necessarily to be erected. But at the end of the nineteenth century a new possibility was revealed. All attempts to establish an electromagnetic theory on a mechanical basis had failed; on the other hand, the electromagnetic theory of Maxwell, amplified and extended from static to moving systems by Lorentz, had acquired a character that seemed to qualify it as at least a rival to mechanics. Instead of a mechanical theory of electricity, an electrical theory of matter claimed the attention of physicists; and the Maxwell-Lorentz electromagnetic equations vied with the mechanical equations of Newton as expressions of the basic laws of the universe.

Unhappily, these sets of equations were incompatible: one could therefore not be derived from the other, so at least one had to go. For instance, Newton's third law of motion, that action and reaction were equal and opposite, was not possible in electromagnetic theory. But the outstanding discrepancy was with Newton's first law, or the principle of relativity, as it had come to be called. That law implied that a state of uniform motion was indistinguishable from another such state and from a state of rest. The Maxwell-Lorentz theory, however, demanded a static ether with respect to which a moving body would exhibit different phenomena from a resting one. Thus, between two electric charges, both at rest in the ether, only an electrostatic force would appear; but if, though still *relatively* at rest, they were moving in the ether, they would constitute two electric currents between which an additional force would operate. It therefore became necessary to determine by experiment whether the various states of uniform motion could indeed be distinguished from one another and from a state of rest. Of the many experiments devised for this purpose we need consider only the most famous, the Michelson-Morley experiment, discussed in this book.

This experiment is now usually looked upon as an attempt

to discover the absolute velocity of the earth, but it was in fact much more fundamental than that. It was an attempt to determine whether the earth, or any other body, had an absolute velocity at all—in other words, whether the Newtonian mechanical theory or the Maxwell-Lorentz electromagnetic theory was to survive. The experiment decided against the Maxwell-Lorentz theory, and this was Michelson's immediate deduction from it. In his paper [3] announcing the result of his first performance of the experiment he wrote: "The interpretation of these results is that there is no displacement of the interference bands. The result of the hypothesis of a stationary ether is thus shown to be incorrect, and the necessary conclusion follows that the hypothesis is erroneous."

This seemed conclusive, but it had the embarrassing consequence of depriving electromagnetism of a most successful theory and leaving nothing in its place. Naturally, therefore, strenuous efforts were made to avoid Michelson's conclusion. The first comprehensive hypothesis to this end was that of Lorentz, who made the *ad hoc* supposition that motion through the ether shortened a body in the direction of motion by a certain factor and reduced the frequency of any vibration it might possess by the same factor. He showed that if this were so, no experiment carried out on any body at all, without reference to anything external, could reveal whether that body was moving or not (although, in fact, there was a real difference between these states) provided that the motion was uniform and that its velocity did not exceed that of light. In mathematical terms, the relation between space and time measurements in relatively moving systems (which became known as the "Lorentz transformation") was such that the electromagnetic equations were invariant to it. The relativity expressed by Newton's first law of motion was therefore, on this view, not a characteristic of nature but a consequence of these ethereal effects on moving bodies which operated so as to hide from view the real state of motion of a body.

Shortly afterward Einstein put forward a different theory.

[3] *American Journal of Science,* XXII (1881), 128.

He was as anxious as Lorentz to save the electromagnetic equations, but he was not willing to sacrifice the principle of relativity as Lorentz had done. He therefore devised his *theory* of relativity, of which the two basic postulates were the *principle* (or *postulate*) of relativity—that all states of uniform motion were intrinsically indistinguishable—and the postulate of constant light velocity—that light emitted in any direction at the same point and at the same instant from each of a number of relatively moving bodies moved through space as a single beam with a fixed velocity c, the motions of the sources having no influence on that of the light emitted.

This seemed merely to express the original contradiction without resolving it. The first postulate granted the validity of the mechanical equations, and the second that of the electromagnetic equations, and these were incompatible. But Einstein sought a reconciliation by accepting the electromagnetic *equations,* with all their metrical consequences, without accepting the *ether* (that is, anything that could serve as a universal standard against which velocity could be measured) which was essential to the electromagnetic *theory*. The rejection of the ether made the relativity postulate a reality instead of the mere appearance that Lorentz' device had made it, but it laid on Einstein the obligation to show how two bodies in relative motion could both be moving with the same velocity c with respect to the same beam of light.

He achieved this through the realization of what no one had noticed before, that no natural method existed for determining the time, according to a given clock, of an event at a distance from that clock. Furthermore, he showed that no unambiguous determination was possible if his postulates were granted, and therefore that the time of such an event had to be *defined* if it was regarded as having any significance. He therefore sought a definition that would justify his postulates. Suppose there are two points, A and B; and pulses of light, traveling as a single pulse, are emitted from sources P and Q when they are both at A, P being stationary there and Q moving toward B. The light will reach B at some particular instant, at which it will be further from P than from Q. An observer with P will therefore consider that the light has traveled further than an observer with Q, and will therefore accord it a higher velocity than the second observer unless the observers allot different times to the arrival of the pulse at B. What Einstein succeeded in doing was to define a procedure for timing that event so that the observers, on applying it, did in fact time the event differently and in such a way that they both arrived at the same velocity for the light. Moreover, that procedure gave the Lorentz transformation for the relation between the times and places of events according to observers in relative motion, so that, quite independently of Lorentz, he reached just that transformation that was needed to preserve the invariance of the electromagnetic equations and so to ensure that, if his theory were correct, no electromagnetic experiment could distinguish between the various states of uniform motion. What Lorentz achieved by arbitrarily postulating physical effects of the ether on moving bodies, Einstein achieved by arbitrarily postulating a certain method of timing distant events. He could therefore dispense with the ether and so retain the postulate of relativity as a fundamental fact of nature instead of a fortuitous consequence of the co-operation of different physical effects.

Since so much has been written in this controversy which shows that the writers have not understood Einstein's theory at all—some of them even think that he discovered the one and only natural way of timing distant events instead of inventing the one needed to save the electromagnetic equations—I quote here his own summary of the theory,[4] specially written to correct this error, for his lectures at Princeton in 1921:

The theory of relativity is often criticized for giving, without justification, a central theoretical rôle to the propagation of light, in that it founds the concept of time upon the law of propagation of light. The situation, however, is somewhat as follows. In order to give

[4] Albert Einstein, *The Meaning of Relativity,* trans. E. P. Adams (Princeton: Princeton University Press, 1955), p. 28.

physical significance to the concept of time, processes of some kind are required which enable relations to be established between different places. It is immaterial what kind of processes one chooses for such a definition of time. It is advantageous, however, for the theory, to choose only those processes concerning which we know something certain. This holds for the propagation of light *in vacuo* in a higher degree than for any other process which could be considered, thanks to the investigations of Maxwell and H. A. Lorentz.

This shows beyond question that it is basic to the theory that the time of a distant event can be chosen as we wish, and that Einstein made his choice in order to justify the Maxwell-Lorentz theory. That means, of course, that the only possible test of the theory must be kinematical; electromagnetic tests will necessarily confirm it since it was framed in order to pass them. It must stand or fall (so far as experiment is concerned) by the comparison of relatively moving clocks and measuring rods to see whether their readings do, in fact, obey the Lorentz transformation. No such test has yet been possible, so the theory remains, like Lorentz', a purely *ad hoc* device to escape from the old predicament. We shall see the significance of this later.

Let us, however, return to the historical development. For years after these two theories (Lorentz' in 1904 and Einstein's in 1905) appeared, they were generally regarded as different forms of the same theory since their mathematical content was the same, notwithstanding that they were physically fundamentally different. Einstein's was truly a relativity theory; Lorentz' was not, though it had some of the consequences of relativity, for example, the impossibility of discovering the state of motion of a body from experiments confined to it. Einstein's theory extended that impossibility to *all* experiments. But the confusion was accentuated by the fact that, although the theory was generally accredited to Lorentz (Einstein's name appears in connection with it very little before World War I) it was given the name "relativity theory," which, in Lorentz' form, it certainly was not. Poincaré, for instance, right up to his death in 1912, habitually referred to "the relativity theory of Lorentz" [5] and scarcely ever, if at all, mentioned Einstein in that connection.

Thus was laid the foundation of a misunderstanding that has bedeviled the subject ever since. When Einstein's *general* relativity theory received confirmation at the eclipse of 1919, it was universally acclaimed as a logical development of his *special* theory of 1905, and the "relativity" theory then began to be ascribed to him alone. But the ideas associated with that name (that is, Lorentz' ideas) through the preceding years then also went over, with the name, to Einstein. The result was a complete confusion. Many physicists regarded the whole thing as metaphysical and, despairing of understanding it, contented themselves with manipulating the equations, which at any rate they could do correctly whatever their meaning might be. The "contraction" of moving bodies, for example, which to Lorentz (and FitzGerald) was an ordinary physical effect like the contraction through cooling, and to Einstein was merely the result of the difference in the times that were regarded as simultaneous by relatively moving observers, was regarded as a single conception, but whether it was "real" or "apparent," or whether there was any longer a difference between reality and appearance, nobody except Lorentz and Einstein seemed to know. By this time nobody in the mathematical-physical world seems to care. A question on such a point is immediately taken as an indication that the questioner does not understand the mathematics, and he is thereupon instructed, politely or sarcastically according to the disposition of the instructor.

Yet the difference between the two theories is perfectly clear, and not in the least degree mystical. It may be illustrated in the simplest way by a single example, which will lead us at once to a solution of "the clock paradox," that is, the relation of relativity to asymmetrical aging. Suppose there are two clocks, A and B, relatively at rest, at widely separated points, and suppose they are synchronized with one another according to Einstein's and Lorentz' prescription. For simplicity, suppose

---

[5] See, for example, Henri Poincaré, *Dernières Pensées* (Paris: Flammarion, 1924), Chap. II.

that, if there is an ether, they are at rest in it. Now let a third clock, *C*, be set to agree with *A* and then moved from the point of *A* to the point of *B* at high uniform speed. On both theories it will read an earlier time than *B* on arrival. On Lorentz' theory this will be because its motion through the ether has retarded its rate of working; on Einstein's theory it will be because the definition by which *B* is set gives it a later time than that of *C*.

We can now see at once that Lorentz' theory requires asymmetrical aging and Einstein's does not. According to the former, the working of Paul's clock is actually slowed down by its motion through the ether, both outward and back, so that it (and Paul) record a shorter time for the journey than Peter and Peter's clock which have not moved. On Einstein's theory, however, there is no ether to do anything to either clock, so each works as though (as in fact is the case on this theory) motion made no difference to it. But what the clock at *B* records can have no effect at all on either Peter or Paul. Hence there is nothing whatever to require asymmetrical aging, and the contrary belief is almost inexplicable.

I say "almost," and not "quite," inexplicable because it is a fact and therefore an explanation must be presumed possible, and also because Einstein, who certainly understood his own theory, held that belief. The attempt to understand that will take us very deep into the heart of the theory itself and show us that, notwithstanding its extreme ingenuity and its apparent success over many decades, it is nevertheless untenable and, moreover, could have been seen to be so at the very beginning. Its disproof does not rest with experiment or with its mathematics, but with an inconsistency in the physical part of the theory; it has physical implications that are both inescapable and incompatible with one another.

Why, then, did Einstein not realize that his theory prohibited asymmetrical aging? In the first place, there is evidence that, although he recognized its fundamental difference from Lorentz', he still thought the observable implications of the two theories were identical. In his first paper on the subject he thought he had proved that his theory required a moving

clock not merely to appear to work more slowly than a stationary one but actually to do so; [6] and, moreover, he must have
seen clearly that unless his theory required everything observable to be exactly the same as though measuring rods and
clocks were physically affected by motion, it would be ineffec-
tive in reconciling mechanics and electromagnetism. Furthermore, when the Peter and Paul problem was first posed—by
Langevin in 1911—there were circumstances that prevented it
from appearing as a serious threat to the relativity theory. To
begin with, the possibility that velocities sufficient to cause an
appreciable difference in rate of aging would ever be attained
was so remote that the problem could not be regarded as other
than a *jeu d'esprit*, in quite a different light from that in
which we see it now. Hence it called for no more than a token
answer, and this was at hand in the circumstance that, in order
to return, Paul would have to undergo an acceleration: the
theory, as it then stood, was applicable only to uniform motions and so was not menaced by this fanciful case.

It is easy to say now that the magnitude of the effect was
immaterial and that it should have been realized that logically
an infinitesimal difference in rate of aging was just as fatal to
the relativity postulate as a very large one. It did not so appear
then, as I, who remember that time, can testify. We are all
human beings whose logic is tempered by imagination, and if
anyone finds it difficult to believe that physicists of genius
could have put aside a logical point merely because its practical implications were negligible, let him reflect on a similar
case. He probably accepts the statistical interpretation of the
laws of thermodynamics, which requires that if a kettle of
water is placed on the fire a large, but finite, number of times,
the water will sometimes freeze. He accepts this because it does
not happen. But the theory makes it just as likely to happen
now as at any other time; suppose, then, he witnesses it to-
morrow. Will he accept it as just a natural exemplification of
the statistical law, or will he look for another cause? At least

---

[6] For a proof that this was erroneous, see H. Dingle, "Special Theory of
Relativity," *Nature,* CXCV (1962), 985.

one eminent physicist, Sir Arthur Eddington, confessed that in such a case he would *reject* the law, which nevertheless he then accepted unreservedly.[7] I do not think we can hold Einstein to have been more disingenuous than any other mathematical physicist, today or at any time.

I think, furthermore, that he was acute enough to realize that unless Peter and Paul aged asymmetrically his theory failed, for the following reason. If they recorded the same time for the journey, that time would certainly have to be either two hundred or two years. The former would be the requirement of Newtonian mechanics, and so could not be that of his own. On the other hand, a journey of two years would lead at once to an impossibility. It is easy to calculate that Paul's speed relative to Peter must be 0.99995 of the speed of light, and the distance traveled must be such that light would have taken 199.99 years to cover it. Hence a beam of light, starting at the same time as Paul, would have moved faster all the way and yet have returned 197.99 years later—a manifest absurdity.

It should cause no surprise, then, that Einstein felt that the technical removal of this problem from the scope of his special theory rendered the problem innocuous. But this escape, of course, was no longer possible when later he generalized the relativity postulate to cover *all* motion.[8] He then realized the dilemma that faced him: if asymmetrical aging was not a possi-

[7] Sir Arthur Stanley Eddington, *New Pathways in Science* (Cambridge: Cambridge University Press, 1935), chap 3.

[8] Nevertheless during a recent controversy many physicists (for example, J. Bronowski, in *The New Scientist,* Aug. 31, 1961) have continued to maintain that Paul's acceleration on reversal prevents the application of the special theory to the problem. Curiously enough, however, they do not therefore refrain from applying it but regard themselves as entitled to use its equations with a meaning of their own in place of that which the relativity postulate gives them. The result—need it be said?—is that asymmetrical aging is "proved" to follow from Einstein's special theory. The reader must be left to appraise this procedure for himself. These writers give no sign that they know of Einstein's rejection of such "proof"—or indeed of much else in the history of the subject.

bility, the special theory failed; if it was, the general postulate failed. He met this situation [9] by accepting asymmetrical aging and invoking "gravitational fields" (using the term in a more general sense than the customary one) to save the relativity postulate, in the following manner.

What has to be shown is that Paul will return younger than Peter, no matter whether the motion is ascribed to one or the other. If it is supposed that Paul moves, he ages slowly, in the manner familiar from the special theory, and whatever effect the acceleration on reversal might have can be ignored by making the journey at uniform motion long enough to produce an overwhelmingly greater effect. He therefore ages by two years while Peter ages by two hundred. But now, the physical conditions being exactly the same, suppose the motion is ascribed to Peter, while Paul remains at rest. Then gravitational fields must be postulated to start, reverse, and stop Peter, while the operation of Paul's engine—which, in the former way of speaking, caused his accelerations—now serves to keep him at rest by neutralizing the effect of the fields. We must now consider the influence of the fields on the aging process. At the beginning and end, when Peter and Paul are close together, this influence will be the same for both, but on reversal of motion they are far apart, in regions of different gravitational potential; and this will make Peter during the reversal age so rapidly compared with Paul as more than to counterbalance his relative slowness of aging during his uniform motion, and leave him at the end with the same difference from Paul as in the former case. The relativity postulate is therefore satisfied. To the criticism that such gravitational fields are pure fictions, Einstein replies that *all* are. The significant difference is not between "real" and "fictitious" fields but between what is *observable* (like the readings of the clocks at separation and reunion) and what is *postulated but not observable* (like the gravitational fields and the relative readings of separated clocks) in order to give a rational description

---

[9] Albert Einstein, "Dialog über Einwände gegen die Relativitätstheorie," *Naturwissenschaften,* VI (1918), 697.

of the process. It is only the former that the relativity postulate requires to be independent of the standard of rest.

This argument is, I think, in principle sound and is legitimately applicable to such a case as that of Foucault's pendulum, in which the gravitational field of the revolving stellar system is called upon to explain the phenomenon when the earth is supposed at rest. But it fails here because the observable phenomena are *not* the same in the two cases. Suppose a clock synchronized with Peter's is placed on the star. When Paul is held to move, his clock is behind this one, by approximately the same amount, when he reaches and when he leaves the star. When Peter and the star are held to move, however, the clock on the star is behind Paul's when it reaches him and ahead when it leaves him. This is an observable difference, so the relativity postulate, which survives a comparison of Peter's and Paul's clocks on their reunion, is by this comparison disproved.

This paper of Einstein's seems to be little known: most of those who try to reconcile asymmetrical aging with relativity use methods that it rules out. The very few writers who adopt Einstein's procedure seem to me to have misunderstood it; they amplify it in a way which Einstein refrained from attempting and which I believe he would have regarded as invalid. A full analysis of this treatment of the problem would, I think, afford great insight into the nature of the relativity of motion, and I have made three unsuccessful attempts to get such an analysis published. The first two were rejected without assigned reason; the third because, it was said, I had "published it all before." It would seem that attempts to elucidate this matter are held to be necessarily evil, and that their suppression is not to be impeded by a misguided regard for accuracy of statement.

Let us, nevertheless, assume here that my syllogism is sound and that in consequence we cannot have both asymmetrical aging and the relativity postulate. Then it follows that the special *theory* of relativity must be rejected: if there is asymmetrical aging, the relativity postulate, which is essential to the theory, is faulted, and if there is no asymmetrical aging, then either Newtonian mechanics is valid or Paul covers a given distance in a shorter time than a faster beam of light. This leads us to seek for the basic error in the theory, for the Peter and Paul problem merely shows that there is such an error but does not locate it.

I think the root of the matter can be best seen in terms of the Minkowski expression of the theory. According to this, the world of nature is represented by a four-dimensional homogeneous mathematical continuum ("space-time"). Everything that happens in nature can be analyzed into "point-events"— that is, events occurring at single points at single instants—and these are represented by points in the continuum. Each such point is uniquely definable by four independent co-ordinates, which can be chosen in various ways. Each choice corresponds to the place (three co-ordinates) and time (one co-ordinate) of a point-event when a particular standard of position, zero of time, and standard of rest are chosen, and any one choice is as valid as any other. The *absolute* position of the event in space-time corresponds to a function of all four co-ordinates which is the same for all co-ordinate systems, and any two events have an absolute separation in space-time though their separations in space and in time vary with the co-ordinate system.

The primary requirement of this theory is that all events are analyzable into occurrences at point-instants, and this is incompatible with the postulate of relativity. To see this we need only consider the simplest possible case, that of two bodies in relative motion. Their motion is an event, and if it is a relation between them, and not a property possessed by each individually, it must occupy the whole space needed for its manifestation, and that is more than a point. The Minkowski concept therefore fails to afford a true representation of nature, and this no matter whether we accept Einstein's or Lorentz' theory. On Einstein's theory it fails because it does not provide for space-extended events; on Lorentz' theory it escapes that disability, for the relative motion, for example, of two bodies *is* made up of their separate individual motions, but it fails because, according to Lorentz, all co-ordinate systems are not equivalent. One is unique—that corresponding to rest in the ether—and a grained, not homogeneous, space-time would be needed to allow for that.

When this is once realized it becomes a simple matter to find cases in which Einstein's theory breaks down. Lest it should seem too abstract, however, let us apply it to a particular case. Suppose a source of monochromatic light, S, and an observer, O, are relatively at rest at a finite distance apart, and let them both be provided with synchronized clocks, and O with a spectroscope in which he observes a spectrum line from the light of S in a certain position. Now suppose that O moves towards S. There are experimental grounds for believing that he will *at once* observe a shift of the spectrum line (the "Doppler effect"). But suppose that, instead of O moving toward S, S moves similarly toward O at the same clock reading: will O observe a spectrum shift at once or later? If the former, an effect of an event at S will be transmitted instantaneously to O, and if the latter we shall have an observational distinction between the motion of O with respect to S and that of S with respect to O. Both conclusions are contrary to the special relativity theory, yet one of them must be realized.

The anomaly appears even more strongly if we suppose that both O and S move similarly, at the same clock reading, in the same direction. If O observes a spectrum shift he can calculate a velocity from it, and that must be an absolute velocity since there is never any relative motion between the only bodies in the system. If he does not observe a spectrum shift, the effect of the motion of S must have been transmitted instantaneously to him, to neutralize the shift he would undoubtedly have seen if S had not moved.

This is entirely equivalent to the example that Einstein himself took at the beginning of his original paper on the subject [10] to show what he meant by his postulate of relativity, namely, that in all cases of relative motion the *phenomena* observed are the same whichever body is moved, although the

[10] "Electrodynamik bewegter Körper," *Annalen der Physik*, XVII (1905), 891.

descriptions of the phenomena may differ. He took the relative motion of a magnet and a coil of wire, in which, in all observable respects, the current produced in the wire is the same whichever is moved. But, according to the theory which he then developed, that is not so if the bodies are far apart. If the coil is moved the current is observed immediately, and if the magnet is moved it is observed later. Synchronized clocks with the bodies would therefore distinguish the cases.

It is easy to see that this is because we are dealing with a phenomenon that, if the relativity postulate is true, necessarily demands a finite space. Either body by itself can be said to rest or to move, and no observation can ban either supposition. It is only when at least two bodies are concerned that motion has meaning, and then a finite region of space must be available. Any phenomenon depending on motion (for example, the Doppler effect or the current in the wire) is therefore irreducible to independent point-events, and the attempt so to reduce it must inevitably conflict with the relativity postulate.

I gave another, equally conclusive, example some years ago [11] in which the attempt to hold to the accepted criterion for synchronizing relatively stationary clocks and to the Lorentz transformation for comparing relatively moving clocks led to the contradiction that each clock could be proved to work both slower and faster than the other. No notice was taken of this, and after a number of repetitions I practically enforced a comment, whereupon the only one worth considering came from Professor Max Born,[12] who stated that I had advanced the wrong problem. He formulated the one I should have proposed and showed that it did not embarrass the theory. Despite an acceptance of this and a further appeal then for attention to my problem, nothing further has happened.

Again the question obtrudes itself: Why, if the special relativity theory is so clearly untenable, has this not been realized

[11] "Relativity and Electromagnetism: an Epistemological Appraisal," *Philosophy of Science*, XXVII (1960), 233.

[12] M. Born, "Special Theory of Relativity," *Nature*, CXCVII (1963), 1287.

before? The answer, I think (I shall consider the implications of this presently), lies fundamentally in the fact that it has become so customary in science to appeal only to experiment and not to trust reason, that even the clearest demonstration of inconsistency in a theory is ineffectual so long as the theory is believed to accord with experiment. The special relativity theory has satisfied this condition in numerous instances during the last fifty years, and accordingly it has acquired an immunity from rational criticism of which physicists seem unaware. In fact, however, there is *no experimental evidence at all* for the theory; all that appears to support it does so through a circular argument. To see this the earliest example will suffice—the Michelson-Morley experiment.

In this experiment, as it is invariably described, the times taken by beams of light to traverse different paths are compared, and an explanation is given in terms of the modification of these times by the motion of the apparatus. Bergson himself (p. 70) accepts this description without question and discusses the effect of motion on clocks attached to the apparatus.

But in fact no clocks at all are used. The experiment is conducted without reference to a clock or to time, so the effect, if any, of motion on clocks cannot account for the observations. We observe only interference fringes, which keep a constant position throughout. How, then, is time introduced into the description? Simply by interpreting the fringes in terms of the Maxwell-Lorentz theory which supposes that they are caused by light having a constant velocity c, a frequency n, and a wave length λ, which are related by the equation, $c = n\lambda$. c and n involve time, and so time enters the description.

But the moment we recall the purpose of the experiment, we see that this is quite illegitimate. It was designed to decide between Newtonian mechanics and the Maxwell-Lorentz electromagnetic theory; we must therefore not presuppose that either of these is true. But that is exactly what has been done. When the Maxwell-Lorentz theory is presupposed, only two explanations are possible: either Newtonian mechanics is wrong or there has been some disturbing factor that has been overlooked. Einstein chose the first alternative and Lorentz the second. The simple, superficial explanation that Michelson automatically adopted, that electromagnetic theory is wrong, is ruled out by the terms in which the experiment is described; it was therefore ignored by everyone except Ritz, who died almost immediately and could therefore be forgotten.

All the supposed experimental evidence for the special relativity theory is of this character; it is a vast assembly of circular arguments posing as experimental verification of a theory of which it shows only a partial internal consistency. To take but one other example, consider the many experiments [13] made to test Einstein's second postulate—that, in accordance with the Maxwell-Lorentz theory, the velocity of light is independent of that of its source. Beams of gamma radiation—which is equivalent to light in this postulate—from hypothetical particles in a vacuum tube, some held to be stationary and others moving at high speed, issue from the tube and their velocities are compared by a highly theoretical technique: the velocities are inferred as equal, and the postulate is "proved." But when we seek for the evidence that the sources have the accepted velocities, we find it in the theory that itself implies the thing to be proved. If the velocity of light is *not* independent of that of its source, that theory is wrong, so the supposed source velocities are meaningless. Furthermore, the quantum theory (which also is implied in the description of the experiment) requires that the "particles" have not the individuality necessary to qualify them as sources for this purpose since they do not obey classical statistics. The whole argument is completely confused. From the only point of view that is legitimate when such an experiment is used as a test of Einstein's postulate, there is but one source of all the radiation emitted—the stationary vacuum tube. Whatever goes on inside it can be determined only theoretically, and to use the theory that is under test to determine it is obviously fallacious.

[13] For example, that of Alväger, Nilsson, and Kjellman, in *Nature*, CXCVII (1963), 1191.

What, now, are we to conclude from all this concerning Bergson's attitude to the relativity theory? In the first place, we must recognize that he saw clearly what to nearly all the physicists was a matter of confusion, namely, that Lorentz' and Einstein's theories were fundamentally distinct. Lorentz' theory was what he called "half-relativity" or "unilateral relativity": Einstein's was "complete relativity" (see especially pp. 91–92). This, in view of the intellectual climate of the time, showed a very clear perception. He had no doubt that, while on Lorentz' theory asymmetrical aging was possible—indeed, inevitable—it was impossible on Einstein's theory, and it was with the latter only that he was here concerned. That in itself must have been sufficient to give him confidence that he understood the matter better than the physicists, to whom the equations were the essential thing and their meaning relatively trivial.

On the other hand—whether through modesty or oversight of what must have appeared to him unimportant compared with his intense awareness of the vital character of time and the inertness of space—Bergson was willing to grant the physicists everything they claimed that did not directly menace his own philosophy. Insofar as time had spatial qualities he was willing for it to be spatialized, and so he failed to see the inherent contradictions in the special relativity theory that would have made it unnecessary for him to defend his philosophy against it. In that defense he accordingly used reasoning that failed to convince the physicists because it missed the point to which they attached importance. Since the time that Peter ascribed to Paul was not the time that Paul lived, he called it a phantom, that is, something unreal, because, as he insisted, only what is perceptible is real (for example, see p. 108), and he likened it to the diminished size which a distant object seems to possess but which corresponds to nothing observable at the position of that object. The analogy is good up to a point, but it breaks down precisely where it is most needed. The physicist could retort—and in these days of automation the retort comes even more readily to mind—that *all* life could be removed from the proceedings. Properly adjusted clocks could be stationed at the points considered; the traveling clock, having been set, could be moved mechanically; and all the necessary readings could be recorded automatically and examined afterwards by anyone at leisure: the readings of Paul's clock would then be no more and no less a phantom than those of Peter's.

It was really not necessary for Bergson to claim a distinction between them. His philosophy did not necessarily demand that, even between two events at the same place, two living persons present at both must have "lived" the same time. He would doubtless have admitted that, if one of them had taken certain drugs, both his mental experiences and his physiological state might have corresponded to a greater degree of aging than that shown by the other, and if drugs could produce that effect, why might not motion? On Lorentz' theory it certainly would, and he was not contesting Lorentz' theory. "Living time," in Bergson's sense, is necessarily an attribute of an individual, and a comparison between the living times of different individuals can show nothing that invalidates a philosophy concerned with its intrinsic nature alone.

We see the same unnecessary disputation in the discussion of the two simultaneities—"intuitive" and "learned." Here Bergson and Einstein were, in fact, in complete agreement. The only absolute simultaneity, according to both, was that of events at the same place, and it was a basic requirement of Einstein's theory—and the most striking evidence of his insight—that the simultaneity of separated events could be only a matter of voluntary definition. There was no difference at all here between them except that, owing to their different points of view, Bergson stressed the intuitive simultaneity of coincident events and Einstein the learned simultaneity of separated events. They were simply calling attention to different sides of the same coin.

It is not my purpose, or within my competence, to attempt an evaluation of Bergson's philosophy in the light of present knowledge, but I think it may be said that, beyond doubt, it is no longer menaced by the physical considerations against which he defends it in this book and which may well have been responsible for the fall in esteem that it suffered as the relativity theory became established. Indeed, we may go further. I think there can now be no doubt that the "space-time," which seemed to Bergson on philosophical grounds to be merely an artificial construction, is in fact just that. The many mystical ideas that have been built on the supposed discovery that there is in nature some objective thing called "space-time," while space and time are merely the subjective products of our arbitrary analysis of this "reality"—these ideas can now be dismissed as purely fictional. "Space-time" is a mathematical conception formed by combining the co-ordinates (x, y, z, t) occurring in the electromagnetic equations. How those co-ordinates are in fact related to our measurements of space and time remains to be discovered, but we can say with certainty that they cannot be *identified* with those measurements. If Lorentz' theory is correct, they correspond to the readings of distorted instruments, and it is the distortions, and not the quantities that we try to measure, that are related with one another in the supposedly inseparable way. If, on the other hand, the electromagnetic equations are fundamentally wrong, then "space-time" is merely a characteristic of a false theory— a conception needed to preserve that theory from immediate disproof. Only further experiment can tell us which of these alternatives is correct, and the most promising of such experiments would be a properly designed determination of the relation of the velocity of light to that of its source.

We still await the performance of such an experiment, but there is no doubt about the attitude of Bergson to this situation: he would certainly have expected Lorentz' theory to be disproved. Another way of expressing the choice, as we have seen, is that it lies between a nonrelativistic world in which motion can be analyzed into a succession of points occupied at successive instants (Lorentz' theory) and a relativistic world in which motion is not so analyzable. Bergson emphatically favoured the second alternative,[14] and he would therefore have been compelled to reject Lorentz' theory. The relativity postulate, on the other hand, while perhaps not essential to his philosophy, is in complete harmony with it. When the necessary experiment is performed, therefore, it should provide some real physical evidence concerning the Bergsonian philosophy in place of the false attack he had to meet.

Turning from the future to the past, however, we may say that in one fundamental respect the influence on philosophy of the schools generated by relativity theory has been unfortunate. Bergson was concerned with experience, as essential philosophy must ever be—in his case pre-eminently with the experience of the passage of time. Physics also is concerned with experiences, but with relatively trivial ones, that is, those amenable to measurement.[15] But the effect of the relativity theory on philosophy has been to concentrate attention on the instruments used to represent experiences by concepts—in particular, languages—as though they were the ultimate objects of philosophical thought. This is the counterpart of the situation in science, in which mathematics is in the saddle and rides physics, so that, for example, Lorentz' and Einstein's theories are thought to be identical because they have the same mathematical structure. The only difference is that while the linguistic philosophers allow their symbols to say nothing, the mathematicians make theirs talk nonsense. This is not to decry the study of languages—it is a necessary study—but when we allow it to release us from the duty of saying something until we have solved all the problems they present, which in all likelihood we shall never do, we go badly astray. If only as a corrective of that, a revival of interest in Bergson's philosophy would be salutary.

14 See, for example, Henri Bergson, *An Introduction to Metaphysics,* trans. T. E. Hulme, "The Library of Liberal Arts," No. 10 (New York: The Liberal Arts Press, Inc., 1955), p. 42.

15 Physics is not to be identified with science, of which it is only a part: science extends beyond the study of measurements.

There is, however, another, still more serious, issue raised by the history of the relativity theory, which is of such vital concern to us all that it cannot pass unnoticed in this connection though I can only touch on it very briefly here. Science (and philosophy also, for in this respect they are alike) depends on complete obedience to the demands of experience and reason. We must accept whatever experience reveals to us, and the theories we form to rationalize it must be logically impeccable. In principle this has always been acknowledged, but in science, because of its history—modern science began largely as a revolt against the undue neglect of experience in philosophy—the assessment of theories has been left almost entirely to experience. Imagination has been allowed to lead the theoretical scientist into various fields of conceivability, notwithstanding that no proof is immediately available that they are, in fact, realizable in experience. Hence the scientist has not been dismayed, but rather exhilarated, by the co-existence of mutually incompatible theories concerned with the same set of phenomena, because he has had implicit faith in the ability of experience (observation or experiment) ultimately to reveal which of them is false.

The method is ideal, so long as the time available is unlimited and the experiments harmless. Indeed, so perfect is it that there has been no need to examine the internal structure of a theory with much care: give it rein, whatever it might be, and experience will ultimately dispose of it if it is unsound. It is true that some theories can be ruled out at once because they are internally inconsistent, for although no theory can be proved right by reason alone, it might be proved wrong by reason alone. But science—in the past perhaps with much wisdom—has thought it better to let wheat and tares grow together until the harvest than to risk destroying wheat through a premature purification. Accordingly, there has developed in the scientific world an attitude of tolerance toward fanciful speculations, especially if they are adorned by an array of mathematical formulae, which might in the future acquire a support from experience that they cannot yet claim, and at the same time an unwillingness to abandon theories that have proved useful, no matter what logical defects they might contain. However reprehensible this might appear from a detached philosophical point of view, it has had at least the justification of assured ultimate success.

The momentous fact, however, which is not yet realized, is that within the last generation this method has ceased to be permissible. The fanciful speculations just referred to, which are most evident at the present time in the field of cosmology, are of relatively slight importance. They merely waste time and money and mislead the public harmlessly for a time on matters in which the interest of the public is ephemeral; they may be allowed to enjoy their fanfare and no irreparable damage is done. The continued adherence to logically disprovable theories, however, is another matter. Certainly, experiment, as well as reason, can be trusted to disprove them; but, scientific experiments being what they now are, they may do so at the cost of a major catastrophe. To experiment now on the basis of a false theory, trusting that Truth is great and shall prevail, is to overlook one thing—that when this happens there may be none left to care if it prevails or not. Yet that is what now goes on daily in our research establishments.

This is not merely an opinion or a theoretical possibility; it is a manifest fact, freely acknowledged by the mathematical physicists themselves—though, I am sure, without the least idea of what they are acknowledging. No one will question that the special relativity theory lies at the heart of modern scientific predictions or that the course of future development in physics would be profoundly changed if it were seen to be false. A proof that it is false has been given, and the only authoritative answer—from Professor Max Born, who I suppose would be generally acknowledged as the *doyen* of mathematical physicists—is to this effect: "The simple fact that all relations between space co-ordinates and time expressed by the Lorentz transformation can be represented geometrically by Minkowski diagrams should suffice to show that there can be no logical contradiction in the theory." [16] In other words, the fact that a piece of algebra corresponds to a piece of geometry is sufficient to guarantee the tenability of a theory; what the algebraic symbols or the geometrical figures mean in terms of experience, of observation, is irrelevant. On the same principles one could say: the simple fact that the equation $y = ax + b$ can be represented geometrically by a straight line should suffice to show that there can be no logical contradiction in the Aristotelian theory that the path of a projectile is rectilinear. The success of range finding conducted on this basis would give a clear indication of what we are to expect in the not too distant future. There is now no reason at all for doubting that material velocities exceeding that of light are possible and may well be attained before long. In terms of the special relativity theory, however, they will be automatically underestimated. What may happen is anybody's guess.

This situation is a natural, though not an inevitable, development from that which faced Bergson. The danger, which I think he saw instinctively but was not able effectively to avert, was that of mistaking ideas for experiences, symbols for observations. But at that time it was clearly seen by both sides that the relation of symbols to experience was an essential part of the theory, and if it had then been shown, from physical considerations, that Paul would not in fact have aged in the manner that the symbols indicated, the theory would by common consent have been abandoned. That is not so today. Physical considerations now count for nothing; the mathematics is all. If a symbol is given the letter t, then our experiences of time must necessarily follow the course that the symbol takes in the logically impeccable theory.

And nobody minds. Not a single dissentient voice has been raised in response to Professor Born's ruling, and one must conclude—as is indeed evident from other considerations [17]—

---

[16] M. Born, "Special Theory of Relativity," 1287.
[17] For a few of many examples, see Samuel and Dingle, *A Threefold Cord* (London: Allen & Unwin, Ltd., 1961).

that it is the general guiding principle of those who hold our lives in their hands. I have tried to direct attention to the danger inherent in this situation, but without success; my attempt to bring it to the attention of the potential victims has been refused publication by both the scientific and the nonscientific press—the latter understandably, since it must be almost impossible for the layman to believe that the scientist, whose reputation for absolute integrity has become proverbial, can really behave in such a way. Yet it is manifestly so, as anyone who cares to read the literature can verify for himself.

The facts must be faced. To a degree never previously attained, the material future of the world is in the hands of a small body of men, on whose not merely superficially apparent but absolute, intuitive (in Bergson's sense of the word) integrity the fate of all depends, and that quality is lacking. Where there was once intellectual honesty they have now merely the idea that they possess it, the most insidious and the most dangerous of all usurpers; the substitution is shown by the fruits, which are displayed in unmistakable clarity in the facts described here. After years of effort I am forced to conclude that attempts within the scientific world to awaken it from its dogmatic slumber are vain. I can only hope that some reader of these pages, whose sense of reality exceeds that of the mathematicians and physicists and who can command sufficient influence, might be able from the outside to enforce attention to the danger before it is too late.

HERBERT DINGLE

April 1965

Selected Bibliography

ADOLPHE, LYDIE. *L'univers bergsonien*. Paris: La Colombe, 1955.

BECQUEREL, JEAN. "Critique de l'ouvrage *Durée et simultané-ité*," *Bulletin scientifique des étudiants de Paris*, X (March–April 1923), 18–29.

BERGSON, HENRI. "Analyse de l'ouvrage de Guyau, *La Genèse de l'idée de temps*," *Revue philosophique de la France et de l'étranger*, XXXI (1891), 185–190.

——. *Creative Evolution*. Trans. ARTHUR MITCHELL. New York: H. Holt Co., 1911.

——. *The Creative Mind*. Trans. MABELLE L. ANDISON. New York: Philosophical Library, 1946.

——. *An Introduction to Metaphysics*. Trans. T. E. HULME. "The Library of Liberal Arts," No. 10. New York: The Liberal Arts Press, Inc., 1955.

——. *Laughter*. Trans. C. BRERETON and F. ROTHWELL. New York: Macmillan Co., 1911.

——. *Matter and Memory*. Trans. N. M. PAUL and W. J. PALMER. New York: Macmillan Co., 1911.

——. *Mind-Energy*. Trans. H. WILDON CARR. New York: H. Holt and Co., 1920.

——. "Remarques sur la théorie de la relativité" (Minutes from the session of April 6, 1922). *Bulletin de la Société française de Philosophie*, XVII (April 1922), 91–113.

——. "Second Reply to Second Letter of André Metz," *Revue de philosophie*, XXXI (July–August 1924), 437–440.

——. "Les Temps Fictifs et le Temps Réel" (First letter in reply to letter of André Metz), *Revue de philosophie*, XXXI (1924), 241–260.

——. *Time and Free Will*. Trans. F. L. POGSON. New York: Macmillan Co., 1913.

———. *The Two Sources of Religion and Morality.* Trans. R. ASHLEY AUDRA and CLOUDSLEY BRERETON. London: Macmillan and Co., Ltd., 1935.

BERTEVAL, W. "Bergson et Einstein," *Revue philosophique de la France et de l'étranger,* CXXXII (1942), 17–28.

BERTHELOT, RENÉ. "L'espace et le temps chez les physiciens," *Revue de Métaphysique et de Morale,* XVIII (1910), 744–775.

BUSCH, J. J. "Einstein et Bergson, convergence et divergence de leurs idées," *Proceedings of the Tenth International Congress of Philosophy,* ed. E. W. BETH and H. J. POS. Amsterdam: North Holland Publishing Co., 1949.

ČAPEK, MILIČ. "La théorie bergsonienne de la matière et la physique moderne," *Revue philosophique de la France et de l'étranger,* LXXVII (1953), 30–44.

CHEVALIER, JACQUES. *Henri Bergson.* Trans. LILIAN A. CLARE. New York: Macmillan Co., 1928.

CRAWFORD, FRANK S., JR. "Experimental Verification of the 'Clock Paradox' of Relativity," *Nature,* CLXXIX (January 5, 1957), 35–36.

DINGLE, HERBERT. "The 'Clock Paradox' of Relativity," *Nature,* CLXXIX (April 27, 1957), 1242. This article is a reply to CRAWFORD (noted above).

———. "The Clock Paradox of Relativity," *Science,* CXXVII (January 17, 1958), 156–157. This article is a reply to McMILLAN (noted below).

———. "Relativity and Space Travel," *Nature,* CLXXVII (April 28, 1956), 782–783. See McCRAE (noted below).

———. "Scientific and Philosophic Implications of the Special Theory of Relativity" in *Albert Einstein: Philosopher-Scientist.* Ed. PAUL ARTHUR SCHILPP. Evanston, Ill.: The Library of Living Philosophers, 1949. Pp. 537–554.

———. *Through Science to Philosophy.* Oxford: The Clarendon Press, 1937.

EINSTEIN, ALBERT. *Relativity: The Special and General Theory*. Trans. ROBERT W. LAWSON. New York: Peter Smith, 1920.

——. *The Meaning of Relativity*. Trans. E. P. ADAMS. Princeton: Princeton University Press, 1955.

GUILLAUME, EDOUARD. "La question du temps d'après Bergson," *Revue générale des sciences*, XXXIII (October 30, 1922), 573–582.

HEIDSIECK, FRANÇOIS. *Henri Bergson et la notion d'espace*. Paris: Le Circle du Livre, 1957.

JANKÉLÉVITCH, VLADIMIR. *Bergson*. Paris: F. Alcan, 1931.

LANGEVIN, PAUL. "L'Évolution de l'espace et temps," *Revue de Métaphysique et de Morale*, XIX (1911), 455–466.

LOVEJOY, ARTHUR O. "The Paradox of the Time-Retarding Journey," *The Philosophical Review*, XL (1931), 48–68 and 152–167.

McCRAE, W. M. "Criticism of Herbert Dingle's Article 'Relativity and Space Travel,'" *Nature*, CLXXVII (April 28, 1956), 783–784.

McMILLAN, EDWIN M. "The 'Clock Paradox' and Space Travel," *Science*, CXXVI (August 30, 1957), 381–384.

METZ, ANDRÉ. *La relativité, exposé sans formules des théories d'Einstein et réfutation des erreurs contenues dans les ouvrages les plus notoires (Durée et simultanéité)*." Preface by BECQUEREL. Paris: E. Chiron, 1923.

——. "Le Temps d'Einstein et la philosophie: à propos de l'ouvrage de M. Bergson, *Durée et simultanéité*," *Revue de philosophie*, XXXI (1924), 56–58.

VOISINE, G. "La durée des choses et la relativité. À propos d'un livre recent de Bergson," *Revue de philosophie*, XXII (1922), 498–522.

WATANABE, SATOSI. "Le concept de temps en physique moderne et la durée pure de Bergson," *Revue de Métaphysique et de Morale*, LVI (1951), 128–142.

Note on the Translation

THE PRESENT translation is taken from the fourth edition of *Durée et Simultanéité* as published by the Librairie Félix Alcan in 1929. The fourth edition is a reprint of the second edition of 1923, which must be considered Bergson's definitive text. All Bergson's footnotes have been translated; footnotes in brackets are those of the translator and are intended to clarify Bergson's text. The mathematical formulae and the diagrams are taken directly from the French text.

DURATION AND SIMULTANEITY

Foreword to the Second Edition
(1923)

THE TEXT of this second edition is the same as that of the first, but we have added three Appendixes intended to overcome certain objections or, rather, to correct certain misunderstandings. The first Appendix has reference to "the journey in the projectile," the second, to the reciprocity of acceleration, and the third, to "proper-time" and "World-line." Despite the diversity of their titles, all three are concerned with the same subject and reach the same conclusion. They plainly demonstrate that, as far as time is concerned, there is no difference between a system endowed with any motion whatever and one in uniform translation.

Preface

A FEW words about the origin of this work will enable the reader to understand its purpose. We began it solely for our own benefit. We wanted to find out to what extent our concept of duration was compatible with Einstein's views on time. Our admiration for this physicist, our conviction that he was giving us not only a new physics but also certain new ways of thinking, our belief that science and philosophy are unlike disciplines but are meant to implement each other, all this imbued us with the desire and even impressed us with the duty of proceeding to a confrontation. But our inquiry soon appeared to hold more general interest. Our concept of duration was really the translation of a direct and immediate experience. Without involving the hypothesis of a universal time as a necessary consequence, it harmonized quite naturally with this belief. It was therefore very nearly the popular idea with which we were going to confront Einstein's theory. And the way this theory appears to come into conflict with common opinion then rose to the fore: we would have to dwell upon the "paradoxes" of the theory of relativity, upon multiple times that flow more or less rapidly, upon simultaneities that become successions, and successions simultaneities, whenever we change our point of view. These theses have a clearly defined physical meaning; they state what Einstein, in an intuition of genius, read in Lorentz' equations. But what is their philosophical meaning? To get at this, we went over Lorentz' formulae term by term, seeking the concrete reality, the perceived or perceptible thing, to which each term corresponded. This examination gave us a quite unexpected result. Not only did Einstein's theses no longer appear to contradict the natural belief of men in a single, universal time but they even corroborated it, accompanied it with prima facie evidence. They owed their paradoxical appearance merely to a misunderstanding. A confusion seemed to have arisen, not in the case of Einstein himself, to be sure, nor among the physicists who were making use physically of his method but among some who were giving this physics, just as it stood, the force of a philosophy. Two different conceptions of relativity, one abstract and the other full of imagery, one incomplete and the other finished, co-existed in their minds and interfered with one another. In clearing up this confusion, we did away with the paradox. It seemed useful to report this. We would thus be helping to clear up the theory of relativity for the philosopher.

But, more than anything else, the analysis with which we had felt obliged to proceed made the salient features of time and its role in the physicist's calculations stand out more sharply. It thus turned out to complete, not just confirm, what we had of old said about duration. No question has been more neglected by philosophers than that of time; and yet they all agree in declaring it of capital importance. This is because they begin by ranking space with time; then, having thoroughly studied the one (generally, space), they leave it to us to treat the other similarly. But we shall not arrive at anything that way. The analogy between time and space is, in fact, wholly external and superficial. It is the result of our using space to measure and symbolize time. If we are guided by this analogy, therefore, if we are to go looking in time for features like those of space, it is at space that we shall stop, at space that covers time and represents it visually for our convenience—we shall not have pushed on to time itself. What would we not gain, however, in recapturing it! The key to the most difficult philosophical problems lies there. We had in the past extended an effort in that direction. The theory of relativity has supplied us with the occasion for resuming it and carrying it a bit further.

Such are the two reasons that lead us to publish the present study. It bears, as we can see, upon a clearly delimited subject.

We have carved out of the theory of relativity that which concerns time; we have laid the other problems aside. We thus remain within the framework of special relativity. Moreover, the theory of general relativity is itself about to enter there, when it wants one of the co-ordinates to represent actual time.

CHAPTER ONE

Half-Relativity

The Michelson-Morley experiment; half or "unilateral" relativity; concrete meaning of terms entering into the Lorentz formulae; expansion of time; breakup of simultaneity; longitudinal contraction

THE THEORY of relativity, even the "special" one, is not exactly founded on the Michelson-Morley experiment, since it expresses in a general way the necessity of preserving a constant form for the laws of electromagnetism when we pass from one system of reference to another. But the Michelson-Morley experiment has the great advantage of stating the problem in concrete terms and also of spreading out the elements of its solution before our very eyes. It materializes the difficulty, so to speak. From it, the philosopher must set forth; to it he will continually have to return, if he wishes to grasp the true meaning of time in the theory of relativity. How often has not this meaning been described and commented upon! Yet it is necessary that we do so once more, for we are not going to adopt straight off the interpretation given it today by the theory of relativity, as is usually done. We want to save all the transitions between common-sense time and Einstein's. We must therefore replace ourselves in the state of mind in which we were to be found in the beginning, when we believed in a motionless ether, in absolute rest, and yet had to account for the Michelson-Morley experiment. We shall thus obtain a certain conception of time which is half-relativist, one-sided, not yet Einstein's, but with which we consider it essential to be acquainted. The theory of relativity may ignore it as much as it likes in its properly scientific inferences; it still undergoes its influence, we believe, as soon as it stops being a physics to become a philosophy. This, it appears to us, is where those paradoxes, which have so alarmed some, so beguiled others, come from. They stem from an ambiguity. They arise from the fact that two mental views of relativity, one radical and conceptual, the other less thoroughgoing and full of imagery, accompany each other in our minds without our realizing it, and that the concept undergoes contamination by the image.

Let us then schematically describe the experiment set up by the American physicist, Michelson, as early as 1881, repeated

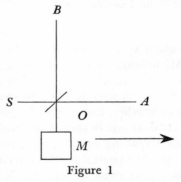

Figure 1

by him and Morley in 1887, and recommenced with even greater care by Morley and Miller in 1905. A beam of light *SO* (figure 1) from source *S* is divided, at point *O*, by a thin glass plate inclined at an angle of 45° to the beam's direction, into two beams one of which is reflected perpendicularly from *SO* in the direction *OB*, while the other continues along the prolongation *OA* of *SO*. At points *A* and *B*, which we shall suppose equidistant from *O*, are two mirrors perpendicular to *OA* and *OB*. The two beams, reflected from mirrors *B* and *A* respectively, return to *O*. The first, passing through the glass plate, follows line *OM*, the prolongation of *BO*; the second is reflected from the plate along the same line *OM*. They are thus superimposed, yielding a system of interference bands which can be observed from point *M* in a lens sighted along *MO*.

Suppose for a moment that the apparatus is not in translation in the ether. It is evident at once that, if the distances OA and OB are equal, the time taken by the first beam to travel from O to A and return is equal to the time taken by the second beam to travel from O to B and return, since the apparatus is motionless in a medium in which light is propagated with the same speed in all directions. The appearance of the interference bands will therefore remain the same for any rotation of the device. It will be the same, in particular, for a 90° rotation which will cause OA and OB to change places with one another.

But, in reality, the apparatus has been involved in the earth's orbital motion.[1] It is easy to see that, this being so, the double journey of the first beam ought not to take as long as the double journey of the second.[2]

Let us indeed calculate, by the usual kinematics, the duration of each of the double passages. With a view to simplifying the exposition we shall grant that the direction SA of the beam of light has been so chosen as to be the same as that of the earth's motion through the ether. We shall call v the speed of the earth, c the speed of light, and l the common length of the two lines OA and OB. The speed of light with respect to the apparatus will be $c - v$ in the passage from O to A. It will be $c + v$ for the return. The time taken by light to go from O to A and back again will then be equal to $\dfrac{l}{c-v} + \dfrac{l}{c+v}$, that is, to $\dfrac{2lc}{c^2 - v^2}$, and the path traversed by this beam in the ether to $\dfrac{2lc^2}{c^2 - v^2}$ or $\dfrac{2l}{1 - \dfrac{v^2}{c^2}}$. Let us now consider the passage of the beam

---

[1] The earth's motion may be thought of as a rectilinear, uniform translation during the course of the experiment.

[2] It will not do to forget, in all that is about to follow, that the radiations emitted from source S are immediately deposited in the motionless ether and are, consequently, in terms of their propagation, independent of the motion of their source.

that goes from the glass plate O to the mirror B and returns. Since the beam of light is moving from O to B at speed c, but, on the other hand, the apparatus is traveling at speed v in the direction OA perpendicular to OB, the relative speed of the beam of light is now $\sqrt{c^2 - v^2}$; and, consequently, the time taken for the entire distance covered is $\dfrac{2l}{\sqrt{c^2 - v^2}}$. This is what we would see again, without directly considering the composition of speeds in the following manner. When the beam returns to the glass plate, the latter is at O' (figure 2) and the beam has touched the mirror when the latter was at B', the triangle $OB'O'$ being, moreover, plainly isosceles. Let us then

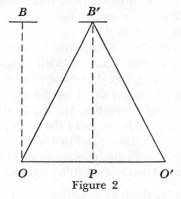

Figure 2

drop a perpendicular $B'P$ from point B' to line OO'. As the distance covered in the $OB'O'$ passage has taken the same time as the OO' distance covered, we have $\dfrac{OB'O'}{c} = \dfrac{OO'}{v}$, that is, $\dfrac{OB'}{c} = \dfrac{OP}{v}$. As we also have $\overline{OB'^2} = l^2 + \overline{OP^2}$, we obtain, by transferring into this last equality the value of OP derived from the first: $OB' = \dfrac{lc}{\sqrt{c^2 - v^2}}$. The time for the distance covered over line $OB'O'$ is therefore indeed $\dfrac{2l}{\sqrt{c^2 - v^2}}$, and the distance actually covered in the ether, $\dfrac{2lc}{\sqrt{c^2-v^2}}$, or $\dfrac{2l}{\sqrt{1-\dfrac{v^2}{c^2}}}$. This

amounts to saying that the earth's motion through the ether affects the two passages differently and that if a rotation imparted to the device leads its arms, OA and OB, to change places with one another, a shift in the interference bands ought to be observed. But nothing of the sort happens. The experiment, repeated at different times of the year, for different speeds of the earth with respect to the ether, has always given the same result.[3] Things happen as if the two double passages were equal, as if the speed of light with respect to the earth were constant, in short, as if the earth were motionless in the ether.

Here, then, is the explanation offered by Lorentz, one that also occurred to another physicist, Fitzgerald. According to them, the line OA would contract as the result of its motion in such a way as to re-establish equality between the two double passages. If the length of OA, which was l when at rest,

becomes $l\sqrt{1-\dfrac{v^2}{c^2}}$ when this line moves at speed v, the distance covered by the beam through the ether will no longer be meas-

ured as $\dfrac{2l}{1-\dfrac{v^2}{c^2}}$, but as $\dfrac{2l}{\sqrt{1-\dfrac{v^2}{c^2}}}$, and the two passages will be

found equal in actuality. It is therefore necessary to assume that any object moving with any speed v undergoes a contraction in the direction of its motion such that its new dimension

is to the old in the ratio of $\sqrt{1-\dfrac{v^2}{c^2}}$ to unity. Of course, this

contraction overtakes the ruler with which we measure the object as well as the object itself. It thus escapes the terrestrial

[3] It has been carried out under such precise conditions, moreover, that any difference between the two passages of light could not fail to appear.

observer. But we would become aware of it if we were in a fixed observatory, the ether.[4]

More generally, let us call S a system motionless in the ether, and S', another example of this system, a double, which was first at one with it and then broke away in a straight line at speed v. Immediately on parting, S' contracts in the direction of its motion. Everything not perpendicular to its direction of motion shares the contraction. If S was a sphere, S' will be an ellipsoid. This contraction explains why the Michelson-Morley experiment gives the same results as if light had a constant speed equal to c in all directions.

But it is also necessary to know why we ourselves, in our turn, measuring the speed of light by terrestrial experiments such as those of Fizeau and Foucault, always get the same figure c no matter what the earth's speed may be with respect to the ether.[5] The observer motionless in the ether will explain it thus: in experiments of this type, the beam of light always makes the double trip of departure and return between point O and another point, A or B, on earth, as in the Michelson-Morley experiment. In the eyes of the observer who shares the earth's motion, the distance of this double journey is therefore 2l. Now, we say that he always finds the same speed c for light. Always, therefore, the clock consulted by the experimenter at point O shows that the same interval t, equal to $\frac{2l}{c}$, has elapsed between the departure and return of the beam. But the ob-

[4] It seems at once that instead of a longitudinal contraction, a transverse expansion could just as well have been assumed, or even one or the other by turns, in due proportion. Regarding this point, as many others, we have been obliged to bypass the explanations given by the theory of relativity. We are confining ourselves to what concerns our present inquiry.

[5] It is indeed important to note (though often omitted) that the Lorentz contraction is not enough to establish, from the standpoint of the ether, the complete theory of the Michelson-Morley experiment performed on earth. We must add to it the lengthening of time and the breakup of simultaneities, all of which we shall rediscover, after transposition, in Einstein's theory. The point has been well clarified in an interesting article by C. D. Broad, "Euclid, Newton, and Einstein," *Hibbert Journal* (April 1920).

server stationed in the ether, eyeing the beam's passage in that medium, believes that the distance covered is really $\dfrac{2l}{\sqrt{1-\dfrac{v^2}{c^2}}}$. He sees that if the moving clock recorded time like the motionless one beside him, it would show an interval $\dfrac{2l}{c\sqrt{1-\dfrac{v^2}{c^2}}}$. Since it nevertheless shows only $\dfrac{2l}{c}$, it is because its time is elapsing more slowly. If, in the same spatial interval between two events, a clock ticks off a fewer number of seconds, each of them lasts longer. The second of the clock attached to the moving earth is therefore longer than that of the stationary clock in the motionless ether. Its duration is $\dfrac{1}{\sqrt{1-\dfrac{v^2}{c^2}}}$. But the earth-dweller is not aware of this.

More generally, let us again call S a system motionless in the ether and S' a double of this system, which at first coincided with it and then broke away in a straight line at speed v. As S' contracts in the direction of its motion, its time expands. An individual attached to system S, perceiving S' and fixing his attention upon a clock-second in S' at the exact moment of the doubling, would see the second of S growing longer in S' like an elastic band being stretched, like an arrow seen under a magnifying glass. Let us understand: no change has taken place in the clock's mechanism or functioning. The phenomenon has nothing to do with the lengthening of a pendulum. It is not because clocks go more slowly that time has lengthened; it is because time has lengthened that clocks, remaining as they are, are found to run more slowly. As the result of motion, a longer, drawn-out, expanded time comes to occupy the spatial interval between two positions of the clock hand. The same slowing, moreover, obtains for every motion and change in the system, since each of them could equally well become representative of time and be given the status of a clock.

We have just been assuming, it is true, that the terrestrial observer followed the departure and return of the beam of light from O to A and from A to O, and measured the speed of light without having to consult any other clock than the one at point O. What would happen if one were to measure this speed only on departure, in that case consulting two clocks [6] located at points O and A respectively? It is, in truth, the beam's double journey that is measured in any terrestrial measurement of light. The experiment of which we speak has therefore never been performed. But nothing proves it unrealizable. We are going to show that it would still give us the same figure for the speed of light. But, to that end, let us recall what the agreement of our clocks consists of.

How do we synchronize two clocks located at different places? By a communication established between the two individuals entrusted with the synchronizing. But, there is no instantaneous communication; and, since every transmission takes time, we have had to select one that is carried out under unchanging conditions. Only signals emitted through the ether meet this requirement: all transmission through ponderable

---

[6] It goes without saying that, in this paragraph, we are giving the name of clock to any device allowing us to measure an interval of time or to situate two instants in exact relation to one another. In experiments relating to the speed of light, Fizeau's cogged wheel and Foucault's turning mirror are clocks. Still more general will be the meaning of the word in the context of the present study. It will be applied to a natural process as well. The turning earth will be a clock.

Moreover, when we speak of the zero of one clock and of the operation by which we determine the zero point of another clock so as to obtain their agreement, it is only for the sake of greater definiteness that we bring in dials and hands. Given any two time-measuring devices whatever, natural or artificial, given, consequently, two motions, we shall be able to choose arbitrarily any point on the path of the first moving body as the point of origin and call it zero. The setting of zero on the second device will consist simply of marking, on the path of the second moving body, the point deemed to correspond to the same instant. In short, the "setting of zero" will have to be understood, in what follows, as the real or ideal operation, carried out or merely thought, whereby two points denoting an original simultaneity will have been marked on the two devices respectively.

matter depends upon the state of that matter and the myriad circumstances that modify it at every moment. It is therefore by means of optical, or, more generally, electromagnetic, signals that the two operators have been obliged to communicate with each other. The individual at O has dispatched to the one at A a beam of light intended to return to him immediately. And things have turned out as they did in the Michelson-Morley experiment, with the difference, however, that mirrors have been replaced by people. There had been an understanding between the two operators at O and A that the latter would mark a zero at the point where the hand of his clock would be at the precise instant at which the beam would reach him. Consequently, the former had only to mark on his clock the beginning and end of the time interval taken up by the beam's round trip: it is in the middle of this interval that he has situated the zero of his clock, since he wished the two zeros to mark "simultaneous" moments and the two clocks to agree from then on.

However, this procedure would be perfectly fine only if the signal's journey were the same leaving as returning or, in other words, if the system to which clocks O and A are attached were motionless in the ether. Even in a moving system, it would still be fine for the synchronizing of two clocks O and B situated on a line perpendicular to the direction of its path; we know, in fact, that if the motion of the system leads O to O', the beam of light makes the same run from O to B' as from B' to O', the triangle $OB'O'$ being isosceles. But it is different in the case of the signal's transmission from O to A and vice versa. The observer who is at absolute rest in the ether believes that the passages are unequal, since in the first journey the beam emitted from point O must chase after point A which is fleeing it, while on the return trip the beam sent back from point A finds point O coming to meet it. Or, if you prefer, he takes note that the distance OA, supposedly identical in both cases, has been cleared by light at the relative speed of $c - v$ in the first, and $c + v$ in the second, so that the times for the distances covered are as $c + v$ to $c - v$. In marking the zero in the middle of the interval traversed by the clock hand between the beam's departure and return, it is being placed, as our motionless observer sees it, too close to the point of departure. Let us calculate the amount of the error. We said just before that the interval traversed by the clock hand on the dial during the round trip is $\frac{2l}{c}$. If, then, at the moment of the signal's emission, a provisional zero has been marked at the point where the clock hand was, it is at point $\frac{l}{c}$ of the dial that there will have been placed the definitive zero M that corresponds, it is believed, to the definitive zero of the clock at A. But the motionless observer knows that if the definitive zero of the clock at O is really to correspond to that of the clock at A, to be simultaneous with it, it would have had to be placed at a point that divided the time interval $\frac{2l}{c}$ not into equal parts but into parts proportional to $c+v$ and $c-v$. Let us call x the first of these two parts. We shall have $\dfrac{x}{\dfrac{2l}{c}-x}=\dfrac{c+v}{c-v}$ and therefore

$x=\frac{l}{c}+\frac{lv}{c^2}$, which amounts to saying that, for the motionless observer, the point M where the definitive zero has been marked is $\frac{lv}{c^2}$ too close to the provisional zero and that, if it is desired to leave it where it is, the definitive zero of the clock at A must be pushed back by $\frac{lv}{c^2}$ in order to have a real simultaneity between the definitive zeros of the two clocks. In short, the clock at A is always an $\frac{lv}{c^2}$ dial interval slower than the time it ought to show. When the clock hand is at the point that we shall agree to call t' (we reserve the designation t for the time of the clocks motionless in the ether), the motionless observer tells himself that if it really agreed with the clock at O, it would show

$t'+\frac{lv}{c^2}$.

In that case, what will happen when operators, respectively located at O and A, wish to measure the speed of light by noting on the synchronized clocks at those points the moment of departure, the moment of arrival and, consequently, the time that light takes to leap the interval?

We have just seen that the zeros of the two clocks have been so placed that, to anyone considering the clocks as agreeing, a light ray always appears to take the same time in going from O to A as in returning to it. Our two physicists will therefore naturally find that the time for the journey from O to A, computed by means of the two clocks located at O and A respectively, is equal to half the round trip's total time, as computed on the clock at O alone. But, we know that the duration of this round trip, computed on the clock at O, is always the same, whatever the speed of the system. It will therefore be so again for the duration of the single trip computed by this new procedure with two clocks: the constancy of the speed of light will again be established. However, the motionless observer in the ether will be following what has been happening from point to point. He will realize that the distance covered by the beam from O to A is proportional to the distance covered from A to O in the ratio of $c + v$ to $c - v$, instead of being equal. He will find that, as the zero of the second clock does not agree with that of the first, the departure and return times, which seem equal when the two clock readings are compared, are really as $c + v$ to $c - v$. There has therefore occurred, he will reflect, an error in the length of the distance traveled and an error regarding the duration of the journey, but the two errors offset each other because it is the same double error that earlier presided at the synchronization of the two clocks.

Thus, whether we compute time on only one clock in a particular place or whether we use two clocks at a distance from each other, we obtain the same figure for the speed of light within the moving system S'. Observers attached to the moving system will judge that the second experiment confirms the first. But our motionless spectator, based in the ether, will simply conclude that he has two corrections to make instead of one for everything relating to the time shown by the clocks of system S'. He had already found that these clocks were running too slowly. He will now reflect that, in addition, the clocks ranged along its direction of motion lag behind one another. Suppose once more that the moving system S' has been separated, as a double, from the motionless system S, and that the dissociation has taken place just as a clock C'_0 in moving system S', coinciding with clock C_0 in system S, pointed, like it, to zero. Let us then consider a clock C'_1 in system S' so placed that the straight line $\overrightarrow{C'_0 \, C'_1}$ indicates the direction of the system's motion, and let us call l the length of this line. When clock C'_1 shows time t', the motionless observer rightly reflects that, since clock C'_1 has lagged behind clock C'_0 of this system by a dial interval of $\dfrac{lv}{c^2}$, there has really elapsed a $t' + \dfrac{lv}{c^2}$ number of seconds in system S'. But, having observed the slowing of time resulting from motion, he already knew that each of those seeming seconds is equal to $\dfrac{1}{\sqrt{1 - \dfrac{v^2}{c^2}}}$ of a real second. He will therefore calculate that if clock C'_1 gives a reading of t', the time really elapsed is $\dfrac{1}{\sqrt{1 - \dfrac{v^2}{c^2}}}\left(t' + \dfrac{lv}{c^2}\right)$. Moreover, at that moment consulting one of the clocks of his motionless system, he will find that the time t which it shows actually is that figure.

But, even before having become aware of the correction needed to pass from time t' to time t, he had perceived the error that is committed inside the moving system in the judging of simultaneity. He had grasped it while watching the synchronizing of the clocks. Let us indeed consider, on the indefinitely extended line $C'_0 \, C'_1$ of this system, a great number of clocks C'_0, C'_1, C'_2, etc., separated by equal intervals of l. When S' coincided with S and therefore happened to be motionless in the ether, the optical signals that came and went between two successive clocks made equal trips in both directions. If all the clocks thus synchronized showed the same time, it really was at the same instant. Now that S' has separated from S as a result of the doubling, the individual in S', who is unaware of being in motion, leaves his clocks C'_0, C'_1, C'_2, etc., as they were; he thinks he has real simultaneities when the clock hands point to the same dial numeral. Moreover, if he has any doubt, he proceeds anew to his synchronizing; he simply finds the confirmation of what he had observed in the motionless state. But the motionless onlooker, who sees how the optical signal now takes a longer path in going from C'_0 to C'_1, from C'_1 to C'_2, etc., than in returning from C'_1 to C'_0, from C'_2 to C'_1, etc., realizes that to have real simultaneity when the clocks show the same time, the zero of clock C'_1 would have to be turned back by $\dfrac{lv}{c^2}$, the zero of clock C'_2 by $\dfrac{2lv}{c^2}$, etc. Simultaneity has changed from real to nominal. It has been incurvated into succession.

To sum up, we have just been trying to discover why light could have the same speed for both the stationary and the moving observer: the investigation of this point has revealed that a system S', born of the doubling of a system S, and moving in a straight line at a speed v, underwent singular modifications. We would formulate them as follows:

1. All lengths in S' have contracted in the direction of its motion. The new length is proportional to the old in the ratio of $\sqrt{1 - \dfrac{v^2}{c^2}}$ to unity.

2. The time of the system has expanded. The new second is proportional to the old in the ratio of unity to $\sqrt{1 - \dfrac{v^2}{c^2}}$.

3. What was simultaneity in system S has generally become succession in system S'. Only those contemporaneous events in S remain contemporaneous in S' which are situated in the same plane perpendicular to the S system's direction of motion. Any

other two events, contemporaneous in S, have separated in S' by $\frac{lv}{c^2}$ seconds of system S', if by l we mean their distance apart computed in the direction of motion of their system, that is, the distance between the two planes, perpendicular to this direction, which pass through each of them respectively.

In short, considered in space and time, system S' is a double of system S which, spatially, has contracted in the direction of its motion, and, temporally, expanded each of its seconds; and which, finally, has broken up into succession in time every simultaneity between two events whose distance apart has narrowed in space. But these changes escape the observer who is part of the moving system. Only the stationary observer is aware of them.

I shall in that case assume that those two well-known observers, Peter and Paul, are able to communicate with each other. Peter, who knows what has been going on says to Paul: "The moment you separated from me, your system flattened out, your time swelled, your clocks disagreed. Here are the correction formulae which will enable you to get back to the truth. It is up to you to see what you can do with them." It is obvious that Paul would reply: "I shall do nothing, because, if I used these formulae, everything in my system would, practically and scientifically, become incoherent. Lengths have shrunk, say you? But then the same is true for the meter that I lay alongside them; and, as the standard of these lengths in my system is their relation to the meter thus altered, that standard must remain what it was. Time, you say further, has expanded and you count more than one second while my clocks tick off just one? But, if we assume that S and S' are two copies of the planet earth, the S' second, like that of S, is by definition a certain fixed fraction of the planet's period of rotation; and say what you will about their not having the same duration, they both still last only one second. Have simultaneities become successions? Do all three clocks situated at points C'_1, C'_2, C'_3 point to the same time when there are three different moments? But at the different moments at which they point to the same time in my system, events occur at points C'_1, C'_2, C'_3 of my system which were legitimately designated contemporaneous in system S; I shall then still agree to call them contemporaneous in order not to have to take a new view of the relations of these events first among themselves, and then with all the others. I shall thereby preserve all their sequences, relations and explanations. In naming as succession what I called simultaneity, I would have an incoherent world or one built on a plan utterly different from yours. In this way, all things and all relations among things will retain their size, remain within the same frames, come under the same laws. I can therefore act as if none of my lengths had shrunk, as if my time had not expanded, as if my clocks agreed. So much, at least, for ponderable matter, for what I carry along with me in the motion of my system; drastic changes have occurred in the temporal and spatial relations of its parts, but I am not, nor need I be, aware of them.

"Now, I must add that I regard these changes as fortunate. In fact, getting away from ponderable matter, what would not my predicament be with regard to light, and, more generally, electromagnetic events, had my space and time dimensions remained as they were! These events are not carried along in the motion of my system, not they. It makes no difference that light waves and electromagnetic disturbances originate in a moving system: the experiment proves that they do not adopt its motion. My moving system drops them off on the way, so to speak, into the motionless ether, which takes charge of them from then on. Even if the ether did not exist, it would be invented in order to symbolize the experimentally established fact of the independence of the speed of light from the motion of the source that emitted it. Now, in this ether, before these optical facts, in the midst of these electromagnetic events, you sit motionless. But I pass through them, and what you perceive from your fixed observatory happens to appear quite differently to me. The science of electromagnetism, which you have so laboriously built up, would have been mine to remake: I would have had to modify my once-established equations for each new speed in my system. What would I have done in a universe so constructed? At the price of what liquidation of all science would the soundness of its temporal and spatial relations have been bought! But thanks to the contraction of my lengths, the expansion of my time, the breakup of my simultaneities, my system becomes, with respect to electromagnetic phenomena, the exact imitation of a stationary system. No matter how fast it travels alongside a light wave, the latter will always maintain the same speed in relation to it, the system will be as if motionless with respect to the light wave. All is then for the best, and a good genie has arranged things this way.

"There is, nevertheless, one case in which I shall have to take your information into account and modify my measurements. This is in the matter of framing a unified mathematical representation of the universe, that is, of everything happening in all the worlds moving with respect to you at every speed. In order to establish this representation which would give us, once complete and perfect, the relation of everything to everything else, we shall have to define each point in the universe by its distances x, y, z from three given planes at right angles, which we shall declare motionless, and which will intersect on axes OX, OY, OZ. Moreover, axes OX, OY, OZ, which will be chosen in preference to all others as the only axes really and not conventionally motionless, will be given in your fixed system. But, in the moving system in which I happen to be, I shall relate my observations to axes $O'X'$, $O'Y'$, $O'Z'$, which are borne along with this system; and, as I see it, it is by its distances x', y', z' from the three planes intersecting on those lines that every point in my system will be defined. Since it is from your motionless point of view that the global representation of the All has to be framed, I must find a way to relate my observations to your axes OX, OY, OZ, or, in other words, to set up equations by means of which I shall once and for all be able, knowing x', y', z', to calculate x, y, z. But this will be easy, thanks to the information you have just given me. First, to simplify matters, I shall assume that my axes $O'X'$, $O'Y'$, $O'Z'$ coincided with yours before the dissociation of the two worlds S and S' (which for the clarity of the present demonstration it will this time be better to make completely different from one another), and I shall also assume that OX and, consequently, $O'X'$ denote the actual direction of motion of S'. This being so, it is clear that planes $Z'O'X'$ and $X'O'Y'$ simply glide over planes ZOX and XOY respectively, that they ceaselessly coincide with them and that consequently y and y' are equal, as are z and z'. We are then left to calculate x. If, from the moment O' leaves O, I compute a time t' on the clock at point x', y', z', I naturally think of the distance from this point to plane ZOY as equal to $x' + vt'$. But in view of the contraction to which you call my attention, this length $x' + vt'$ would not coincide with your x but with $x\sqrt{1 - \dfrac{v^2}{c^2}}$ and consequently what you call x is $\dfrac{1}{\sqrt{1 - \dfrac{v^2}{c^2}}} (x' + vt')$. This solves the problem. I shall not forget, moreover, that the time t', which has elapsed for me and which my clock at point x', y', z' shows me, is different from yours. When this clock gave me the t' reading, the time t shown by yours was, as you stated, $\dfrac{1}{\sqrt{1 - \dfrac{v^2}{c^2}}}\left(t' + \dfrac{vx'}{c^2}\right)$. Such is the time t which I shall show you. For time as for space, I shall have gone over from my point of view to yours."

That is how Paul would reply. And he would at the same time have laid down the famous "transformation equations" of Lorentz, equations which, moreover, if we assume Einstein's more general standpoint, do not imply that system S is definitely stationary. In fact, we shall soon demonstrate how, after Einstein, we can make S any system at all, provisionally immobilized by the mind, and how it is then necessary to attribute to S', considered from the point of view of S, the same temporal and spatial distortions that Peter attributed to Paul's system. In the hypothesis, hitherto always accepted, of a single time and of a space independent of time, it is obvious that if S' moves with respect to S at the constant speed v, if x', y', z' are the distances from a point M' in the system S' to the three planes determined by the three axes $O'X'$, $O'Y'$, $O'Z'$, each at right angles to the other two, and if, finally, x, y, z are the distances from this same point to the three fixed rectangular planes with which the three moving planes were at first merged, we have

$$x = x' + vt'$$
$$y = y'$$
$$z = z'.$$

Moreover, as the same time always unfolds in every system, we get

$$t = t'.$$

But, if motion brings about contractions in length, a slowing of time, and causes the clocks of the time-expanded system to show only a local time, there ensue explanations between Peter and Paul until we have

$$x = \frac{1}{\sqrt{1 - \dfrac{v^2}{c^2}}}\,(x' + vt')$$

(1)
$$y = y'$$
$$z = z'$$
$$t = \frac{1}{\sqrt{1 - \dfrac{v^2}{c^2}}}\left(t' + \frac{vx'}{c^2}\right).$$

Hence we have a new formula for the composition of speeds. Let us, in fact, imagine point M' moving with uniform motion inside S', parallel to $O'X'$ at speed v' measured, of course, by $\dfrac{x'}{t'}$. What will be its speed for the observer in S who refers the successive positions of the moving point to his axes OX, OY, OZ? To find this speed v'', measured by $\dfrac{x}{t}$, we must divide the first by the fourth of the above equations member by member, getting

$$v'' = \frac{v + v'}{1 + \dfrac{vv'}{c^2}}$$

although up till now mechanics laid down that

$$v'' = v + v'.$$

Accordingly, if S is a river bank and S' a boat sailing at speed v with respect to the bank, a passenger walking its deck at speed v' in its direction of motion would not have, in the eyes of the motionless observer on the shore, speed $v + v'$, as was hitherto believed, but a speed less than the sum of the two component speeds. At least, that is how things look at first. In reality, the resultant speed is truly the sum of the two component speeds, if the speed of the passenger on the boat is measured from the bank, like the speed of the boat itself. Measured from the boat, the speed v' of the passenger is $\frac{x'}{t'}$ if, say,

the length that the passenger finds the boat to be (a constant length, since the boat is always at rest for him) is called x' and the time he takes to walk it, t', that is, the difference between his times of departure and arrival as shown on two clocks placed at its stern and bow respectively (we are imagining an immensely long boat whose clocks could only have been synchronized by signals transmitted at a distance). But, for the observer motionless on the bank, the boat contracted when it passed from rest to motion, time expanded on it, its clocks no longer agreed. In his eyes, the distance walked off on the boat by the passenger is therefore no longer x' (if x' were the length of the quay with which the motionless boat coincided),

but $x' \sqrt{1 - \dfrac{v^2}{c^2}}$; and the time taken to cover this distance is not

t' but $\dfrac{1}{\sqrt{1 - \dfrac{v^2}{c^2}}} \left(t' + \dfrac{vx'}{c^2} \right)$. He will conclude that the speed to be

added to v in order to get v'' is not v' but

$$\frac{x' \sqrt{1 - \dfrac{v^2}{c^2}}}{\dfrac{1}{\sqrt{1 - \dfrac{v^2}{c^2}}} \left(t' + \dfrac{vx'}{c^2} \right)}$$

that is,

$$\frac{v'\left(1 - \dfrac{v^2}{c^2}\right)}{1 + \dfrac{vv'}{c^2}}.$$

He will then have

$$v'' = v + \frac{v'\left(1 - \dfrac{v^2}{c^2}\right)}{1 + \dfrac{vv'}{c^2}} = \frac{v + v'}{1 + \dfrac{vv'}{c^2}}.$$

We see thereby that no speed can exceed that of light, every composition of any speed v' with a speed v assumed equal to c always resulting in this same speed c.

Such are the formulae, therefore—to come back to our first hypothesis—which Paul will have in mind when he wishes to pass from his point of view to Peter's and thus obtain (every observer attached to every moving system S'', S''', etc., having done as much) a unified mathematical representation of the universe. If he could have established his equations directly, without Peter's intervention, he could just as well have supplied them to Peter in order to allow him, knowing x, y, z, t, v'', to calculate x', y', z', t', v'. Let us indeed solve the equations in (1) for x', y', z', t', v'; we shall at once derive

$$x' = \frac{1}{\sqrt{1 - \dfrac{v^2}{c^2}}}(x - vt)$$

$$y' = y$$
$$z' = z$$

(2)

$$t' = \frac{1}{\sqrt{1 - \dfrac{v^2}{c^2}}}\left(t - \dfrac{vx}{c^2}\right)$$

$$v' = \frac{v'' - v}{1 - \dfrac{vv''}{c^2}}$$

equations which are more usually presented as the Lorentz transformation.[7] But this is of small concern at the moment.

[7] It is important to point out that, if we have just reconstituted the Lorentz equations in the course of commenting upon the Michelson-

In rediscovering these equations term by term, in defining the perceptions of observers placed in one or the other system, we only wished to set the stage for the analysis and demonstration that form the subject of the present work.

Morley experiment, it was with a view to showing the concrete meaning of each of the terms that compose them. The fact is that the transformation group discovered by Lorentz assures, in a general manner, the invariance of electromagnetic equations.

CHAPTER TWO

Complete Relativity

Concerning the reciprocity of motion; relativity, no longer "unilateral" but "bilateral"; interference of this first hypothesis with the second: ensuing misunderstandings; relative and absolute motion; propagation and conveyance; systems of reference; from Descartes to Einstein

WE HAVE momentarily slipped from the point of view which we shall call that of "unilateral relativity" to that of reciprocity, which is Einstein's own. Let us hurry back to our position. But let us say right now that the contraction of bodies in motion, the expansion of their times, the breakup of simultaneity into succession will be retained in Einstein's theory just as they are: there will be nothing to change in the equations we have just worked out or, more generally, in what we said about system S′ in its temporal and spatial relations with system S. Only, these contractions in size, expansions of time, and breakups of simultaneity will become explicitly reciprocal (they are already so implicitly, from the very form of the equations), and the observer in S′ will repeat for S everything the observer in S had asserted about S′. There will then disappear, as we shall also show, what was at first paradoxical in the theory of relativity: we claim that a single time and an extension independent of duration continue to exist in Einstein's theory considered in its pure state; they remain what they have always been for common sense. But it is practically impossible to arrive at the theory of a double relativity without passing through that of a single relativity, where one still posits an absolute point of reference, a motionless ether. Even when we *conceive* relativity in the second sense, we still *see* it a little in the first; for say as we will that only the reciprocal motion of S and S' with respect to one another exists, we do not investigate this reciprocity without taking one of the two terms, S or S', as our "system of reference"; but, as soon as a system has been thus immobilized, it temporarily becomes an absolute point of reference, a substitute for the ether. In brief, absolute rest, expelled by the understanding, is reinstated by the imagination. From the mathematical standpoint, there is no objection to this. Whether system S, adopted as a system of reference, is at absolute rest in the ether, or whether it is at rest solely with respect to every system with which we compare it, in both cases the observer located in S will treat alike the measurements of time which will be transmitted to him from every system such as S'; in both cases, he will apply Lorentz' transformation equations to them. The two theories are equivalent for the mathematician. But the same is not true for the philosopher. For if S is at absolute rest and all other systems are in absolute motion, the theory of relativity will actually imply the existence of multiple times, all on the same footing and all real. But if, on the other hand, we subscribe to Einstein's theory, the multiple times will remain; but there will never be more than a single real one among them, as we propose to demonstrate; the others will be mathematical fictions. That is why, in our opinion, if we adhere strictly to Einstein's theory, all the philosophical difficulties relative to time disappear, and so too will all the oddities that have led so many minds astray. We need not, therefore, dwell upon the meaning to assign the "distortion of bodies," the "slowing of time," and the "rupture of simultaneity" when we believe in the existence of a motionless ether and a privileged system. It will be enough to try to find out how we ought to understand them in Einstein's theory. Then, casting a backward glance over the first point of view, we shall realize that we had to take that position at first, and we shall consider natural the temptation to return to it even though we have adopted the second; but we shall also see how false problems arise from the fact alone that images have been borrowed from the one to nourish the abstractions corresponding to the other.

We have imagined a system S at rest in the motionless ether, and a system S' in motion with respect to S. But, the ether has never been perceived; it has been introduced into physics as a prop for calculations. On the other hand, the motion of a system S' with respect to system S is an observed fact. We must also consider as a fact, until proven otherwise, the constancy of the speed of light in a system that changes speed at our bidding and whose speed can therefore drop to zero. Let us now return to the three assertions with which we set out: (1) S' shifts with respect to S, (2) light has the same speed in both systems, (3) S is stationed in a motionless ether. It is clear that two of these express facts, and the third, a hypothesis. Let us reject the hypothesis: we now have no more than the two facts. But, in that case, the first one will no longer be formulated in the same way. We stated that S' shifts with respect to S; why did we not just as readily declare S to be shifting with respect to S'? Simply because S was judged to be sharing the absolute immobility of the ether. But there is no longer any ether,[1] no

[1] We are, of course, speaking only of a fixed ether, constituting a privileged, unique, absolute system of reference. But the ether theory, properly amended, may very well be picked up again by the theory of relativity. Einstein is of this opinion (see his lecture of 1920 on "The Ether and The Theory of Relativity"). To preserve the ether, the attempt had already been made to use some of Larmor's ideas (cf. Ebenezer Cunningham, *The Principles of Relativity* [Cambridge: University Press, 1914], Chap. XV).

[The lecture by Einstein to which Bergson refers was delivered on May 5, 1920, at the University of Leyden. It has been translated by G. B. Jeffrey and W. Perret, along with two other lectures, in *Sidelights on Relativity* (London: Methuen, 1922). In this lecture Einstein sums up his view as follows: "Recapitulating, we may say that, according to the general theory of relativity, space is endowed with physical qualities. In this sense, therefore, there exists an ether. According to the general theory of relativity, space without ether is unthinkable, for, in such space, there not only would be no propagation of light, but also no possibility of existence for standards of space and time (measuring-rods and clocks), nor therefore any space-time intervals in the physical sense. But this ether may

longer absolute stability anywhere. We shall therefore be able to say, as we please, that S' is moving with respect to S or that S is moving with respect to S', or rather that S and S' are moving with respect to one another. In short, what is actually given is a reciprocity of displacement. How could it be otherwise, since the motion perceived in space is only a continual variation of distance? If we consider two points A and B and the positional change of "one of them," all that the eye perceives and science can note is the change in the distance between them.[2] Language will express this fact in the statement that A moves or that B does. It has the choice; but it would be still closer to experience to say that A and B move with respect to one another, or, more simply, that the distance between A and B grows shorter or longer. The "reciprocity" of motion is therefore a fact of observation. We could state it a priori as a condition of science, because science works only with measurements—measurement generally bears upon lengths; and when a length increases or decreases, there is no reason for privileging one of its extremities; all we can assert is that the distance between the two grows shorter or longer.[3]

To be sure, it is far from true that every motion is reducible to what is perceived of it in space. In addition to motions we observe only from without, there are also those we are conscious of producing. When Descartes spoke of the reciprocity of motion,[4] it was not without justice that More replied, "If I am sitting quietly, and someone else, moving a thousand paces away from me, reddens with fatigue, it is certainly he

---

not be thought of as endowed with the quality characteristic of ponderable media, as consisting of parts which may be tracked through time. The idea of motion may not be applied to it" (pp. 23–24).]

2 We called attention to this point and to that of the "reciprocity" of motion in *Matière et mémoire* (*Matter and Memory*) (Paris: F. Alcan, 1896), Chap. IV; and in *Introduction à la métaphysique* (*Introduction to Metaphysics*) (first published in *Revue de Métaphysique et de la Morale,* January 1903).

3 On this point see *Matière et mémoire* (*Matter and Memory*), pp. 214ff.

4 Descartes, *Principles*, II, 29.

who moves and I who rest." [5] All that science can tell us of the relativity of the motion perceived by our eyes and measured by rulers and clocks will leave untouched our deep-seated feeling of going through motions and exerting efforts whose dispensers we are. Let the "quietly seated" More decide to run in his turn, let him get up and run: no matter how much we insist that his running is a reciprocal place-changing of his body and the ground, that he is in motion if our thought immobilizes the earth, but that it is the earth that moves if we consider the runner motionless, he will never accept our ruling; he will always declare that he perceives his act immediately, that this act is a fact, and that the fact is unilateral. All men and probably most animals possess this awareness of resolved-upon and executed movements. And since living beings thus perform motions which really are theirs, which depend solely upon them, which are perceived from within but, considered from without, appear to the eye as nothing more than a reciprocity of displacement, we can guess that it is so with relative motions generally, and that a reciprocity of displacement is the visual manifestation of an absolute internal change occurring somewhere in space. We have dwelt upon this point in a work we titled *Introduction to Metaphysics*. This, in fact, seemed to us to be the function of the metaphysician: he must penetrate into the interior of things; and the true essence, the underlying reality of a motion can never be better revealed to him than when he performs the motion himself, when he doubtless still perceives it from the outside like any other motion, but in addition apprehends it from within as an effort whose track alone was visible. But, the metaphysician obtains this direct, inner, and sure perception only from motions that he himself performs. Only these can he guarantee as real acts, absolute motions. Indeed, in the case of motions performed by other living creatures, it is not by virtue of a direct perception, but by sympathy, by reason of analogy that he gives them the status of independent realities. And concerning the motions of matter in general he can say nothing except that there prob-

[5] H. More, *Scripta Philosophica* (1679), II, 248.

ably are internal changes, analogous or not to efforts, which occur we know not where and which are brought before our eyes, like our own acts, by the reciprocal displacement of bodies in space. We do not therefore have to take absolute motion into account in the construction of science; we know only rarely where it occurs, and, even then, science would have nothing to do with it, for it is not measurable and the business of science is to measure. Science can and must retain of reality what is spread out in homogeneous, measurable space. The motion it studies is therefore always relative and can only consist of a reciprocity of displacement. Whereas More spoke as a metaphysician, Descartes indicated the point of view of science with lasting precision. He even went well beyond the science of his day, beyond Newtonian mechanics, beyond our own, formulating a principle whose demonstration was reserved for Einstein.

For it is a remarkable fact that the radical relativity of motion, postulated by Descartes, could not be categorically asserted by modern science. Science, as we understand it since Galileo, undoubtedly believed motion to be relative. It gladly declared it so. But as a consequence it dealt with it hesitantly and incompletely. There were two reasons for this. First, science runs counter to common sense only when strictly necessary. So, if every rectilinear and nonaccelerated motion is clearly relative, if, therefore, in the eyes of science, the track is as much in motion with respect to the train as the train is with respect to the track, the scientist nonetheless declares that the track is motionless; he speaks like anyone else when he has no interest in expressing himself otherwise. But this is not the main point. The reason that science has never insisted upon the radical relativity of uniform motion is that it felt incapable of extending this relativity to accelerated motion—at least it was obliged to give up the attempt provisionally. More than once in the course of its history it has submitted to a necessity of this sort. From a principle immanent in its method, it sacrifices something to an hypothesis which is immediately verifiable and which gives useful results right away. If the advantage continues, it is because the hypothesis was true in one respect; and consequently, this hypothesis will perhaps one day be found to have definitely contributed to establishing the principle that it had provisionally set aside. It is thus that Newtonian dynamics appeared to cut short the development of Cartesian mechanics. Descartes posited that everything relating to physics is spread out and moving in space; he thereby gave the ideal formula of a universal mechanism. But, to cling to this formula would have meant considering globally the relation of all to all; whereas a solution, albeit provisional, of particular problems could be obtained only by more or less artificially carving out and isolating parts within the whole; but, as soon as relation is neglected, force is introduced. This introduction was only that very elimination; it expressed the necessity, under which the human intellect labors, of studying reality a portion at a time, powerless as it is to form, at one stroke, a combined analytic and synthetic conception of the whole. Newton's dynamics could therefore be—and has indeed turned out to be—a step toward the complete demonstration of Cartesian mechanics, which Einstein has perhaps achieved. But, this dynamics implied the existence of an absolute motion. One could still grant the relativity of motion for non-accelerated rectilinear translation; but the appearing of centrifugal forces in rotational motion seemed to attest that one was now dealing with a true absolute; and that all other accelerated motion was equally to be considered absolute. Such is the theory that remained classic until Einstein. It was, however, not possible to get more than a provisional understanding from it. A historian of mechanics, Mach, had drawn attention to its inadequacy,[6] and his critique certainly helped give rise to new ideas. No philosopher could be entirely satisfied with a theory that regarded mobility as an ordinary relation of reciprocity in the case of uniform motion, and as a reality immanent in a moving body in the case of accelerated motion. If, for our part, we thought it necessary to admit of an absolute change wherever a spatial motion is observed, if we believed

6 Ernst Mach, *Die Mechanik in ihrer Entwicklung,* II, vi.

that the consciousness of effort reveals the absolute character of the attendant motion, we added that the consideration of this absolute motion concerns only our knowledge of the interior of things, that is, a psychology that reaches into metaphysics.[7] We added that, for physics, whose role is to study the relations among visual data in a homogeneous space, every motion *had* to be relative. And yet certain motions *could not* be so. Today they can. If only for this reason, the general theory of relativity marks an important date in the history of ideas. We do not know what final fate physics reserves for it. But, whatever happens, the conception of spatial motion which we find in Descartes, and which harmonizes so well with the spirit of modern science, has been rendered scientifically acceptable by Einstein for accelerated as for uniform motion.

It is true that this part of Einstein's work is the last. It is the "generalized" theory of relativity. The reflections upon time and simultaneity belong to the "special" theory of relativity, the latter being concerned only with uniform motion. But within the special theory there was a kind of demand for the general theory. For despite its being "special," that is, limited to uniform motion, it was not the less *radical*, since it declared motion to be reciprocal. Now, why had one not yet gone that far openly? Why was the idea of relativity applied only hesitantly even to the uniform motion that was declared relative? Because it was feared that the idea would no longer apply to accelerated motion. But, as soon as a physicist regards the relativity of motion as radical, he has to try to envisage accelerated motion as relative. Were it still only for this reason, the special theory of relativity drew in its wake that of general relativity and could appear convincing to the philosopher only by lending itself to this generalization.

But if all motion is relative and if there is no absolute point of reference, no privileged system, the observer inside a system will obviously have no way of knowing whether his system is in motion or at rest. Nay, let us say that he would be wrong

---

[7] *Matière et mémoire (Matter and Memory)*, 214ff. Cf. *Introduction à la métaphysique (Introduction to Metaphysics)*.

to wonder about it, for the question no longer has any meaning; it does not present itself in those terms. He is free to rule whatever he pleases; his system will be motionless, by very definition, if he makes it his "system of reference" and there installs his observatory. This could not be so even in the case of uniform motion when we believed in a motionless ether; it certainly could not be so when we believed in the absolute character of accelerated motion. But as soon as these two theories are discarded, any system is at rest or in motion, as we please. It is, of course, necessary to abide by the choice of the motionless system once made and to treat the others accordingly.

We do not wish to prolong this introduction unduly. We must nevertheless recall what we once said about the idea of body and also of absolute motion; that double series of reflections permitted us to infer the radical relativity of motion as displacement in space. What is immediately given to our perception, we explained, is a continuity of extension upon which qualities are deployed; more especially, it is a visual continuity of extension, and, therefore, of color. There is nothing here of the artificial, conventional, merely human. Colors would probably appear differently to us if our eye and our consciousness were differently formed; nonetheless there would always be something unshakably real which physics would continue to resolve into elementary vibrations. In brief, as long as we speak only of a qualified and qualitatively modified continuity, such as colored and color-changing extension, we immediately express what we perceive, without interposed human convention—we have no reason to suppose that we are not here in the presence of reality itself. Every appearance must be deemed a reality as long as it has not been shown to be illusory, and this demonstration has never been made in an actual case; it was believed to have been made but that was an illusion, as we think we have proven.[8] Matter is therefore immediately presented as a reality. But is this true for a particular body given the status of a more or less independent reality? The

8 *Matière et mémoire* (*Matter and Memory*), pp. 225ff. Cf. Chap. I.

visual perception of a body is the result of our dividing up of colored extension; we have cut it out of the continuity of extension. It is very likely that this fragmentation is carried out differently by different animal species. Many are incapable of going ahead with it; and those who are able to are governed, in this operation, by their type of activity and the nature of their needs. "Bodies," we wrote, "have been cut out of nature's cloth by a *perception* whose scissors follow the stippled lines over which *action* would pass." [9] That is what psychological analysis has to say. And physics confirms it. It dissolves the body into a virtually infinite number of elementary corpuscles; and, at the same time, it shows us this body linked to other bodies by thousands of reciprocal actions and reactions. It thus introduces so much discontinuity into it, and, on the other hand, establishes between it and the rest of things so much continuity that we can gather what there must be of the artificial and conventional in our division of matter into bodies. But, if each body, taken individually and arrested where our habits of perception bound it, is in great part a being of convention, why would this not be so for the motion considered to be affecting this body individually? There is only one motion, we said, which is perceived from within, and of which we are aware as an event in itself: the motion that our effort brings to our attention. Elsewhere, when we see a motion occur, all we are sure of is that some change is taking place in the universe. The nature and even the exact location of this change escape us; we can only note certain changes of position that are its visual and surface aspect, and these changes are necessarily reciprocal. All motion—even ours as perceived from without and made visual—is therefore relative. It goes without saying, moreover, that only the motion of ponderable matter is in question. The analysis just made shows this clearly enough. If color is a reality, so must be the oscillations that somehow occur within it—since they have an absolute charac-

9 *L'Evolution créatrice (Creative Evolution)* (Paris: F. Alcan, 1907), pp. 12, 13. Cf. *Matière et mémoire (Matter and Memory)*, Chap. I and pp. 218ff.

ter, ought we still to call them motions? Furthermore, how can we rank the act by which these real oscillations, elements of a quality and partaking of what is absolute in the quality, are propagated in space with the entirely relative, necessarily reciprocal displacement of two systems S and S' carved more or less artificially out of matter? We speak of motion, here as there; but has the word the same meaning in both cases? Let us rather speak of *propagation* in the first and *conveyance* in the second: it follows from our analyses of old that propagation must be thoroughly distinguished from conveyance. But, then, rejecting the emission theory, the propagation of light not being a translation of particles, we shall not expect the speed of light with respect to a system to vary in accordance with whether the latter is "at rest" or "in motion." Why should it make allowance for a certain entirely human way of perceiving and conceiving things?

Let us then freely take the position of reciprocity. We shall now have to define in a general manner certain terms whose meaning had hitherto seemed sufficiently indicated in each particular case by the very use we made of them. Accordingly, we shall apply the term "system of reference" to the trihedral trirectangle with respect to which we shall agree to situate, by indicating their respective distances from its three faces, all points in the universe. The physicist who is building Science will be attached to this trihedral. The vertex of this trihedral will serve him generally as his observatory. The points of his system of reference will, of course, be at rest with respect to one another. But, it must be added that, in the hypothesis of relativity, the system of reference will itself be motionless all the while it is being used for referring. What, in effect, can the fixity of a trihedral in space be if not a property we bestow upon it, the momentarily privileged situation that we assure it, in adopting it as our system of reference? As long as we retain a stationary ether and absolute positions, immobility belongs to things in earnest; it is not of our decreeing. Once the ether has vanished along with the privileged system and fixed points, only relative motions of objects with respect to one another are left; but, as we cannot move with respect to ourselves, immobility will be, by definition, the state of the observatory in which we shall mentally take our place: there, as a matter of fact, is our trihedral of reference. To be sure, nothing prevents us from imagining, at a given moment, that the system of reference is itself in motion. Physics is often interested in doing so, and the theory of relativity readily makes this assumption. But when the physicist sets his system of reference in motion, it is because he provisionally chooses another, which then becomes motionless. It is true that this second system can in turn be mentally set in motion without thought necessarily electing to settle in a third system. But in that case it oscillates between the two, immobilizing them by turns through goings and comings so rapid that it entertains the illusion of leaving them both in motion. It is in this precise sense that we shall speak of a "system of reference."

On the other hand, we shall apply the term "constant system" or simply "system," to every group of points which retain the same relative positions and which are therefore motionless with respect to one another. The earth is a system. A multitude of displacements and changes no doubt appear on its surface and hide within it; but these motions stay within a fixed frame; I mean that no matter how many relatively fixed points we find on earth we cannot help but be attached to them, the events that unfold in the intervals then passing as mere mental views: the events would be nothing more than images successively combing through the consciousness of motionless observers at those fixed points.

Now a "system" can generally be given the status of a "system of reference." It will be necessary to understand by this that we are agreeing to settle the chosen system of reference in this system. It will sometimes be necessary to indicate the particular point in the system at which we are locating the vertex of the trihedral. More often, this will be unnecessary. Thus, when we shall be taking account only of the state of rest or motion of the system earth with respect to another system, it will be possible to view it as a single physical point; this point will then become the vertex of our trihedral. Or else, allowing the earth its true size, we shall understand that the trihedral is located somewhere upon it.

Moreover, the transition from "system" to "system of reference" will be continuous if we take the position of the theory of relativity. It is, in fact, essential in this theory to disperse an endless number of synchronized clocks, and therefore observers, over its "system of reference." The system of reference can therefore no longer be a single trihedral with a single observer. "Clocks" and "observers" need not be anything physical; by "clock" we simply mean here an ideal recording of time according to definite laws or rules, and by "observer," an ideal reader of this ideally recorded time. It is nonetheless true that we are now picturing the possibility of physical clocks and living observers at every point in the system. The tendency not to differentiate between "system" and "system of reference" was, moreover, immanent in the theory of relativity from the beginning, since it was by immobilizing the earth, by taking this composite system as our system of reference, that the invariability of the result of the Michelson-Morley experiment was explained. In most cases, the assimilation of the system of reference to an aggregate system of this type offers no objection. And it may have great advantages for a philosopher who is trying to find out, for example, in what measure Einstein's times are real times, and who will therefore be obliged to post flesh-and-blood observers, conscious beings, at all the points in the system of reference where there are "clocks."

Such are the preliminary thoughts that we needed to present. We have given them much space. But it was for not having strictly defined the terms used, for not having been sufficiently used to seeing a reciprocity in relativity, for not having constantly borne in mind the relation between the radical and the less thoroughgoing relativity, and for not having been on our guard against a confusion between them, in a word, for not having kept close to the passage from the physical to the mathematical that we have been so seriously mistaken about the philosophical meaning of time in the theory of relativity. Let us add that we have hardly any longer been preoccupied with the nature of time itself. Nevertheless, we had to begin this way. Let us pause at this point. The analyses and distinctions that we have just made, and the reflections on time and its measurement that we are about to present, will make it easy to deal with the interpretation of Einstein's theory.

CHAPTER THREE

Concerning the Nature of Time

Succession and consciousness; origin of the idea of a universal time; real duration and measurable time; concerning the immediately perceived simultaneity: simultaneity of flow and of the instant; concerning the simultaneity indicated by clocks; unfolding time; unfolding time and the fourth dimension; how to recognize real time

THERE IS no doubt but that for us time is at first identical with the continuity of our inner life. What is this continuity? That of a flow or passage, but a self-sufficient flow or passage, the flow not implying a thing that flows, and the passing not presupposing states through which we pass; the *thing* and the *state* are only artificially taken snapshots of the transition; and this transition, all that is naturally experienced, is duration itself. It is memory, but not personal memory, external to what it retains, distinct from a past whose preservation it assures; it is a memory within change itself, a memory that prolongs the before into the after, keeping them from being mere snapshots appearing and disappearing in a present ceaselessly reborn. A melody to which we listen with our eyes closed, heeding it alone, comes close to coinciding with this time which is the very fluidity of our inner life; but it still has too many qualities, too much definition, and we must first efface the difference among the sounds, then do away with the distinctive features of sound itself, retaining of it only the continuation of what precedes into what follows and the uninterrupted transition, multiplicity without divisibility and succession without separation, in order finally to rediscover basic time. Such is immediately perceived duration, without which we would have no idea of time.

How do we pass from this inner time to the time of things? We perceive the physical world and this perception appears, rightly or wrongly, to be inside and outside us at one and the same time; in one way, it is a state of consciousness; in another, a surface film of matter in which perceiver and perceived coincide. To each moment of our inner life there thus corresponds a moment of our body and of all environing matter that is "simultaneous" with it; this matter then seems to participate in our conscious duration.[1] Gradually, we extend this duration to the whole physical world, because we see no reason to limit it to the immediate vicinity of our body. The universe seems to us to form a single whole; and, if the part that is around us endures in our manner, the same must hold, we think, for that part by which it, in turn, is surrounded, and so on indefinitely. Thus is born the idea of a duration of the universe, that is to say, of an impersonal consciousness that is the link among all individual consciousnesses, as between these consciousnesses and the rest of nature.[2] Such a consciousness would grasp, in a single, instantaneous perception, multiple events lying at different points in space; simultaneity would be precisely the possibility of two or more events entering within a single, instantaneous perception. What is true and what illusory, in this way of seeing things? What matters at the moment is not allotting it shares of truth or error but seeing clearly where experience ends and theory begins. There is no doubt that our consciousness feels itself enduring, that our perception plays a

[1] For the development of the views presented here, see *Essai sur les données immédiates de la conscience* (*Time and Free Will*) (Paris: F. Alcan, 1889), mainly Chaps. II and III; *Matière et mémoire* (*Matter and Memory*), Chaps I and IV; *L'Evolution créatrice* (*Creative Evolution*), *passim.* Cf. *Introduction à la métaphysique* (*Introduction to Metaphysics*); and *La perception du changement* (*The Perception of Change*) (Oxford: Oxford University Press, 1911). [The last-named title was republished in Paris in 1934, along with several other essays, under the title *La pensée et le mouvant* and was translated as *The Creative Mind*.]

[2] Cf. those of our works we have just cited.

part in our consciousness, and that something of our body and environing matter enters into our perception.[3] Thus, our duration and a certain felt, lived participation of our physical surroundings in this inner duration are facts of experience. But, in the first place, the nature of this participation is unknown, as we once demonstrated; it may relate to a property that things outside us have, without themselves enduring, of manifesting themselves in our duration in so far as they act upon us, and of thus scanning or staking out the course of our conscious life.[4] Next, in assuming that this environment "endures," there is no strict proof that we may find the same duration again when we change our surroundings; different durations, differently rhythmed, might coexist. We once advanced a theory of that kind with regard to living species. We distinguished durations of higher and lower tension, characteristic of different levels of consciousness, ranging over the animal kingdom. Still, we did not perceive then, nor do we see even today any reason for extending this theory of a multiplicity of durations to the physical universe. We had left open the question of whether or not the universe was divisible into independent worlds; we were sufficiently occupied with our own world and the particular impetus that life manifests there. But if we had to decide the question, we would, in our present state of knowledge, favor the hypothesis of a physical time that is one and universal. This is only a hypothesis, but it is based upon an argument by analogy that we must regard as conclusive as long as we are offered nothing more satisfactory. We believe this scarcely conscious argument reduces to the following: All human consciousnesses are of like nature, perceive in the same way, keep in step, as it were, and live the same duration. But, nothing prevents us from imagining as many human consciousnesses as we please, widely scattered through the whole universe, but brought close enough to one another for any two consecutive ones, taken at random, to overlap the fringes of

3 See *Matière et mémoire* (*Matter and Memory*), Chap. I.
4 Cf. *Essai sur les données immédiates de la conscience* (*Time and Free Will*), especially pp. 82ff.

their fields of outer experience. Each of these two outer experiences participates in the duration of each of the two consciousnesses. And, since the two consciousnesses have the same rhythm of duration, so must the two experiences. But the two experiences have a part in common. Through this connecting link, then, they are reunited in a single experience, unfolding in a single duration which will be, at will, that of either of the two consciousnesses. Since the same argument can be repeated step by step, a single duration will gather up the events of the whole physical world along its way; and we shall then be able to eliminate the human consciousnesses that we had at first laid out at wide intervals like so many relays for the motion of our thought; there will be nothing more than an impersonal time in which all things will pass. In thus formulating humanity's belief, we are perhaps putting more precision into it than is proper. Each of us is generally content with indefinitely enlarging, by a vague effort of imagination, his immediate physical environment, which, being perceived by him, participates in the duration of his consciousness. But as soon as this effort is precisely stated, as soon as we seek to justify it, we catch ourselves doubling and multiplying our consciousness, transporting it to the extreme limits of our outer experience, then, to the edge of the new field of experience that it has thus disclosed, and so on indefinitely—they are really multiple consciousnesses sprung from ours, similar to ours, which we entrust with forging a chain across the immensity of the universe and with attesting, through the identity of their inner durations and the contiguity of their outer experiences, the singleness of an impersonal time. Such is the hypothesis of common sense. We maintain that it could as readily be considered Einstein's and that the theory of relativity was, if anything, meant to bear out the idea of a time common to all things. This idea, hypothetical in any case, even appears to us to take on special rigor and consistency in the theory of relativity, correctly understood. Such is the conclusion that will emerge from our work of analysis. But that is not the important point at the moment. Let us put aside the question of a single time. What we wish to establish is that we cannot speak of a reality that endures without inserting consciousness into it. The metaphysician will have a universal consciousness intervene directly. Common sense will vaguely ponder it. The mathematician, it is true, will not have to occupy himself with it, since he is concerned with the measurement of things, not their nature. But if he were to wonder what he was measuring, if he were to fix his attention upon time itself, he would necessarily picture succession, and therefore a before and after, and consequently a bridge between the two (otherwise, there would be only one of the two, a mere snapshot); but, once again, it is impossible to imagine or conceive a connecting link between the before and after without an element of memory and, consequently, of consciousness.

We may perhaps feel averse to the use of the word "consciousness" if an anthropomorphic sense is attached to it. But to imagine a thing that endures, there is no need to take one's own memory and transport it, even attenuated, into the interior of the thing. However much we may reduce the intensity of our memory, we risk leaving in it some degree of the variety and richness of our inner life; we are then preserving the personal, at all events, human character of memory. It is the opposite course we must follow. We shall have to consider a moment in the unfolding of the universe, that is, a snapshot that exists independently of any consciousness, then we shall try conjointly to summon another moment brought as close as possible to the first, and thus have a minimum of time enter into the world without allowing the faintest glimmer of memory to go with it. We shall see that this is impossible. Without an elementary memory that connects the two moments, there will be only one or the other, consequently a single instant, no before and after, no succession, no time. We can bestow upon this memory just what is needed to make the connection; it will be, if we like, this very connection, a mere continuing of the before into the immediate after with a perpetually renewed forgetfulness of what is not the immediately prior moment. We shall nonetheless have introduced memory. To tell the truth, it is impossible to distinguish between the duration, however short it may be, that separates two instants and a memory that connects them, because duration is essentially a continuation of what no longer exists into what does exist. This is real time, perceived and lived. This is also any conceived time, because we cannot conceive a time without imagining it as perceived and lived. Duration therefore implies consciousness; and we place consciousness at the heart of things for the very reason that we credit them with a time that endures.

However, the time that endures is not measurable, whether we think of it as within us or imagine it outside of us. Measurement that is not merely conventional implies, in effect, division and superimposition. But we cannot superimpose successive durations to test whether they are equal or unequal; by hypothesis, the one no longer exists when the other appears; the idea of verifiable equality loses all meaning here. Moreover, if real duration becomes divisible, as we shall see, by means of the community that is established between it and the line symbolizing it, it consists in itself of an indivisible and total progress. Listen to a melody with your eyes closed, thinking of it alone, no longer juxtaposing on paper or an imaginary keyboard notes which you thus preserved one for the other, which then agreed to become simultaneous and renounced their fluid continuity in time to congeal in space; you will rediscover, undivided and indivisible, the melody or portion of the melody that you will have replaced within pure duration. Now, our inner duration, considered from the first to the last moment of our conscious life, is something like this melody. Our attention may turn away from it and, consequently, from its indivisibility; but when we try to cut it, it is as if we suddenly passed a blade through a flame—we divide only the space it occupied. When we witness a very rapid motion, like that of a shooting star, we quite clearly distinguish its fiery line divisible at will, from the indivisible mobility that it subtends; it is this mobility that is pure duration. Impersonal and universal time, if it exists, is in vain endlessly prolonged from past to future; it is all of a piece; the parts we single out in it are merely those of a space that delineates its track and becomes its equivalent in our eyes; we are dividing the unfolded, not the unfolding. How do we first pass from the unfolding to the unfolded, from pure duration to measurable time? It is easy to reconstruct the mechanism of this operation.

If I draw my finger across a sheet of paper without looking at it, the motion I perform is, perceived from within, a continuity of consciousness, something of my own flow, in a word, duration. If I now open my eyes, I see that my finger is tracing on the sheet of paper a line that is preserved, where all is juxtaposition and no longer succession; this is the unfolded, which is the record of the result of motion, and which will be its symbol as well. Now, this line is divisible, measurable. In dividing and measuring it, I can then say, if it suits me, that I am dividing and measuring the duration of the motion that is tracing it out.

It is therefore quite true that time is measured through the intermediary of motion. But it is necessary to add that, if this measurement of time by motion is possible, it is, above all, because we are capable of performing motions ourselves and because these motions then have a dual aspect. As muscular sensation, they are a part of the stream of our conscious life, they endure; as visual perception, they describe a trajectory, they claim a space. I say "above all" because we could, in a pinch, conceive of a conscious creature reduced to visual perception who would yet succeed in framing the idea of measurable time. Its life would then have to be spent in the contemplation of an outside motion continuing without end. It would also have to be able to extract from the motion perceived in space and sharing the divisibility of its trajectory, the "pure mobility," the uninterrupted solidarity of the before and after that is given in consciousness as an indivisible fact. We drew this distinction just before when we were speaking of the fiery path traced out by the shooting star. Such a consciousness would have a continuity of life constituted by the uninterrupted sensation of an external, endlessly unfolding mobility. And the uninterruption of unfolding would still remain distinct from the divisible track left in space, which is still of the unfolded. The latter is divisible and measurable because it is space. The other is duration. Without the continual unfolding, there would be only space, and a space that, no longer subtending a duration, would no longer represent time.

Now, nothing prevents us from assuming that each of us is tracing an uninterrupted motion in space from the beginning to the end of his conscious life. We could be walking day and night. We would thus complete a journey coextensive with our conscious life. Our entire history would then unfold in a measurable time.

Are we thinking of such a journey when we speak of an impersonal time? Not entirely, for we live a social and even cosmic life. Quite naturally we substitute any other person's journey for the one we would make, then any uninterrupted motion that would be contemporaneous with it. I call two flows "contemporaneous" when they are equally *one* or *two* for my consciousness, the latter perceiving them together as a single flowing if it sees fit to engage in an undivided act of attention, and, on the other hand, separating them throughout if it prefers to divide its attention between them, even doing both at one and the same time if it decides to divide its attention and yet not cut it in two. I call two instantaneous perceptions "simultaneous" that are apprehended in one and the same mental act, the attention here again being able to make one or two out of them at will. This granted, it is easy to see that it is entirely in our interest to take for the "unfolding of time" a motion independent of that of our own body. In truth, we find it already taken. Society has adopted it for us. It is the earth's rotational motion. But if we accept it, if we understand it as time and not just space, it is because a journey of our own body is always virtual in it, and *could have been* for us the unfolding of time.

It matters little, moreover, what moving body we adopt as

our recorder of time. Once we have exteriorized our own duration as motion in space, the rest follows. Thenceforth, time will seem to us like the unwinding of a thread, that is, like the journey of the mobile entrusted with computing it. We shall say that we have measured the time of this unwinding and, consequently, that of the universal unwinding as well.

But all things would not seem to us to be unwinding along with the thread, each actual moment of the universe would not be for us the tip of the thread, if we did not have the concept of simultaneity at our disposal. We shall soon see the role of this concept in Einstein's theory. For the time being, we would like to make clear its psychological origin, about which we have already said something. The theoreticians of relativity never mention any simultaneity but that of two instants. Anterior to that one, however, is another, the idea of which is more natural: the simultaneity of two flows. We stated that it is of the very essence of our attention to be able to be divided without being split up. When we are seated on the bank of a river, the flowing of the water, the gliding of a boat or the flight of a bird, the ceaseless murmur in our life's deeps are for us three separate things or only one, as we choose. We can interiorize the whole, dealing with a single perception that carries along the three flows, mingled, in its course; or we can leave the first two outside and then divide our attention between the inner and the outer; or, better yet, we can do both at one and the same time, our attention uniting and yet differentiating the three flows, thanks to its singular privilege of being one and several. Such is our primary idea of simultaneity. We therefore call two external flows that occupy the same duration "simultaneous" because they both depend upon the duration of a like third, our own; this duration is ours only when our consciousness is concerned with us alone, but it becomes equally theirs when our attention embraces the three flows in a single indivisible act.

Now from the simultaneity of two flows, we would never pass to that of two instants, if we remained within pure duration, for every duration is thick; real time has no instants.

But we naturally form the idea of instant, as well as of simultaneous instants, as soon as we acquire the habit of converting time into space. For, if a duration has no instants, a line terminates in points.[5] And, as soon as we make a line correspond to a duration, to portions of this line there must correspond "portions of duration" and to an extremity of the line, an "extremity of duration"; such is the instant—something that does not exist actually, but virtually. The instant is what would terminate a duration if the latter came to a halt. But it does not halt. Real time cannot therefore supply the instant; the latter is born of the mathematical point, that is to say, of space. And yet, without real time, the point would be only a point, not an instant. Instantaneity thus involves two things, a continuity of real time, that is, duration, and a spatialized time, that is, a line which, described by a motion, has thereby become symbolic of time. This spatialized time, which admits of points, ricochets onto real time and there gives rise to the instant. This would not be possible without the tendency—fertile in illusions—which leads us to apply the motion *against* the distance traveled, to make the trajectory coincide with the journey, and then to decompose the motion over the line as we decompose the line itself; if it has suited us to single out points on the line, these points will then become "positions" of the moving body (as if the latter, moving, could ever *coincide* with something at rest, as if it would not thus stop moving at once!). Then, having dotted the path of motion with positions, that is, with the extremities of the subdivisions of the line, we have them correspond to "instants" of the continuity of the motion—mere virtual stops, purely mental views. We once described the mechanism of this process; we have also shown how the difficulties raised by philosophers over the question of motion vanish as soon as we perceive the relation of the instant to spatialized time, and that of spatial-

---

[5] That the concept of the mathematical point is natural is well known to those who have taught geometry to children. Minds most refractory to the first elements imagine immediately and without difficulty lines without thickness and points without size.

ized time to pure duration. Let us confine ourselves here to remarking that no matter how much this operation appears learned, it is native to the human mind; we practice it instinctively. Its recipe is deposited in the language.

Simultaneity of the instant and simultaneity of flow are therefore distinct but complementary things. Without simultaneity of flow, we would not consider these three terms interchangeable: continuity of our inner life, continuity of a voluntary motion which our mind indefinitely prolongs, and continuity of any motion through space. Real duration and spatialized time would not then be equivalent, and consequently time in general would no longer exist for us; there would be only each one's duration. But, on the other hand, this time can be computed thanks only to the simultaneity of the instant. We need this simultaneity of the instant in order (1) to note the simultaneity of a phenomenon with a clock moment, (2) to point off, all along our own duration, the simultaneities of these moments with moments of our duration which are created in the very act of pointing. Of these two acts, the first is the essential one in the measurement of time. But without the second, we would have no particular measurement, we would end up with a figure t representing anything at all, we would not be thinking of time. It is therefore the simultaneity between two instants of two motions outside of us that enables us to measure time; but it is the simultaneity of these moments with moments pricked by them along our inner duration that makes this measurement one of time.

We shall have to dwell upon these two points. But let us first open a parenthesis. We have just distinguished between two "simultaneities of the instant"; neither of the two is the simultaneity most in question in the theory of relativity, namely, the simultaneity between readings given by two separated clocks. Of that we have spoken in our first chapter; we shall soon be especially occupied with it. But it is clear that the theory of relativity itself cannot help acknowledging the two simultaneities that we have just described; it confines

itself to adding a third, one that depends upon a synchronizing of clocks. Now we shall no doubt show how the readings
of two separated clocks C and C', synchronized and showing
the same time, are or are not simultaneous according to one's
point of view. The theory of relativity is correct in so stating;
we shall see upon what condition. But it thereby recognizes
that an event E occurring beside clock C is given in simultaneity with a reading on clock C in a quite different sense—
in the psychologist's sense of the word simultaneity. And likewise for the simultaneity of event E' with the reading on its
"neighboring" clock C'. For if we did not begin by admitting
a simultaneity of this kind, one which is absolute and has
nothing to do with the synchronizing of clocks, the clocks
would serve no purpose. They would be bits of machinery
with which we would amuse ourselves by comparing them with
one another; they would not be employed in classifying events;
in short, they would exist for their own sake and not to serve
us. They would lose their *raison d'être* for the theoretician
of relativity as for everyone else, for he too calls them in only
to designate the time of an event. Now, it is very true that
simultaneity thus understood is easily established between
moments in two flows only if the flows pass by "at the same
place." It is also very true that common sense and science
itself until now have, a priori, extended this conception of
simultaneity to events separated by any distance. They no
doubt imagined, as we said further back, a consciousness coextensive with the universe, capable of embracing the two events
in a unique and instantaneous perception. But, more than
anything else, they applied a principle inherent in every
mathematical representation of things and asserting itself in
the theory of relativity as well. We find in it the idea that the
distinction between "small" and "large," "not far apart" and
"very far apart," has no scientific validity and that if we can
speak of simultaneity outside of any synchronizing of clocks,
independently of any point of view, when dealing with an
event and a clock not much distant from one another, we have
this same right when the distance is great between the clock

and the event or between the two clocks. No physics, no astronomy, no science is possible if we deny the scientist the right to represent the whole universe schematically on a piece of paper. We therefore implicitly grant the possibility of reducing without distorting. We believe that size is not an absolute, that there are only relations among sizes, and that everything would turn out the same in a universe made smaller at will, if the relations among parts were preserved. But in that case how can we prevent our imagination, and even our understanding, from treating the simultaneity of the readings of two very widely separated clocks like the simultaneity of two clocks slightly separated, that is, situated "at the same place"? A thinking microbe would find an enormous interval between two "neighboring" clocks. And it would not concede the existence of an absolute, intuitively perceived simultaneity between their readings. More Einsteinian than Einstein, it would see simultaneity here only if it had been able to note identical readings on two microbial clocks, synchronized by optical signals, which it had substituted for our two "neighboring" clocks. Our absolute simultaneity would be its relative simultaneity because it would refer our absolute simultaneity to the readings on its two microbial clocks which it would, in its turn, perceive (which it would, moreover, be equally wrong to perceive) "at the same place." But this is of small concern at the moment; we are not criticizing Einstein's conception; we merely wish to show to what we owe the natural extension that has always been made of the idea of simultaneity, after having actually derived it from the ascertainment of two "neighboring" events. This analysis, which has until now hardly been attempted, reveals a fact that the theory of relativity could make use of. We see that if our understanding passes here so easily from a short to a long distance, from simultaneity between neighboring events to simultaneity between widely-separated events, if it extends to the second case the absolute character of the first, it is because it is accustomed to believing that we can arbitrarily modify the dimensions of all things on condition of retaining their relations. But it is time to close the parenthesis. Let us return to the intuitively perceived simultaneity which we first mentioned and the two propositions we had set forth: (1) it is the simultaneity between two instants of two motions outside us that allows us to measure an interval of time; (2) it is the simultaneity of these moments with moments dotted by them along our inner duration that makes this measurement one of time [pp. 52–54].

The first point is obvious. We saw above how inner duration exteriorizes itself as spatialized time and how the latter, space rather than time, is measurable. It is henceforth through the intermediary of space that we shall measure every interval of time. As we shall have divided it into parts corresponding to equal spaces, equal by definition, we shall have at each division point an extremity of the interval, an instant, and we shall regard the interval itself as the unit of time. We shall then be able to consider any motion, any change, occurring beside this model motion; we shall point off the whole length of its unfolding with "simultaneities of the instant." As many simultaneities as we shall have established, so many units of time shall we record for the duration of the phenomenon. Measuring time consists therefore in counting simultaneities. All other measuring implies the possibility of directly or indirectly laying the unit of measurement over the object measured. All other measuring therefore bears upon the interval between the extremities even though we are, in fact, confined to counting these extremities. But in dealing with time, we can only count extremities; we merely *agree* to say that we have measured the interval in this way. If we now observe that science works exclusively with measurements, we become aware that, with respect to time, science counts instants, takes note of simultaneities, but remains without a grip on what happens in the intervals. It may indefinitely increase the number of extremities, indefinitely narrow the intervals; but always the interval escapes it, shows it only its extremities. If every motion in the universe were suddenly to accelerate in proportion, including the one that serves as the measure of time, something would change for a consciousness not bound up with intracerebral molecular motions; it would not receive the same enrichment between sunup and sundown; it would therefore detect a change; in fact, the hypothesis of a simultaneous acceleration of every motion in the universe makes sense only if we imagine a spectator-consciousness whose completely qualitative duration admits of a more or a less without being thereby accessible to measurement.[6] But the change would exist only for that consciousness able to compare the flow of things with that of the inner life. In the view of science nothing would have changed. Let us go further. The speed of unfolding of this external, mathematical time might become infinite; all the past, present, and future states of the universe might be found experienced at a stroke; in place of the unfolding there might be only the unfolded. The motion representative of time would then have become a line; to each of the divisions of this line there would correspond the same portion of the unfolded universe that corresponded to it before in the unfolding universe; nothing would have changed in the eyes of science. Its formulae and calculations would remain what they were.

It is true that exactly at the moment of our passing from the unfolding to the unfolded, it would have been necessary to endow space with an extra dimension. More than thirty years

[6] It is obvious that our hypothesis would lose its meaning if we thought of consciousness as an "epiphenomenon" added to cerebral phenomena of which it would be merely the result or expression. We cannot dwell here upon this theory of consciousness-as-epiphenomenon, which we tend more and more to consider arbitrary. We have discussed it in detail in several of our works, notably in the first three chapters of *Matière et mémoire* (*Matter and Memory*) and in different essays in *L'Energie spirituelle* (*Mind-Energy*). Let us confine ourselves to recalling: (1) that this theory in no way stems from facts, (2) that its metaphysical origins are easily made out, (3) that, taken literally, it would be self-contradictory. (Concerning this last point and the oscillation, which the theory implies between two contrary assertions, see *L'Energie spirituelle* (*Mind-Energy*) (Paris: F. Alcan, 1919), pp. 203–223. In the present work, we take consciousness as experience gives it to us, without theorizing about its nature and origins.

ago,[7] we pointed out that spatialized time is really a fourth dimension of space. Only this fourth dimension allows us to juxtapose what is given as succession: without it, we would have no room. Whether a universe has three, two, or a single dimension, or even none at all and reduces to a point, we can always convert the indefinite succession of all its events into instantaneous or eternal juxtaposition by the sole act of granting it an additional dimension. If it has none, reducing to a point that changes quality indefinitely, we can imagine the rapidity of succession of the qualities becoming infinite and these *points of quality* being given all at once, provided we bring to this world without dimension a line upon which the points are juxtaposed. If it already had one dimension, if it were linear, two dimensions would be needed to juxtapose the *lines of quality*—each one indefinite—which were the successive moments of its history. The same observation again if it had two dimensions, if it were a surface universe, an indefinite canvas upon which flat images would indefinitely be drawn, each one covering it completely; the rapidity of succession of these images will again be able to become infinite, and we shall again go over from a universe that unfolds to an unfolded universe, provided that we have been accorded an extra dimension. We shall then have all the endless, piled-up canvasses giving us all the successive images that make up the entire history of the universe; we shall possess them all together; but we shall have had to pass from a flat to a volumed universe. It is easy to understand, therefore, why the sole act of attributing an infinite speed to time, of substituting the unfolded for the unfolding, would require us to endow our solid universe with a fourth dimension. Now, for the very reason that science cannot specify the "speed of unfolding" of time, that it counts simultaneities but necessarily neglects intervals, it deals with a time whose speed of unfolding we

[7] *Essai sur les données immédiates de la conscience* (*Time and Free Will*), p. 83.

may as well assume to be infinite, thereby virtually conferring an additional dimension upon space.

Immanent in our measurement of time, therefore, is the tendency to empty its content into a space of four dimensions in which past, present, and future are juxtaposed or superimposed for all eternity. This tendency simply expresses our inability mathematically to translate time itself, our need to replace it, in order to measure it, by simultaneities which we count. These simultaneities are instantaneities; they do not partake of the nature of real time; they do not endure. They are purely mental views that stake out conscious duration and real motion with virtual stops, using for this purpose the mathematical point that has been carried over from space to time.

But if our science thus attains only to space, it is easy to see why the dimension of space that has come to replace time is still called time. It is because our consciousness is there. It infuses living duration into a time dried up as space. Our mind, interpreting mathematical time, retraces the path it has traveled in obtaining it. From inner duration it had passed to a certain undivided motion which was still closely bound up with it and which had become the model motion, the generator or computer of time; from what there is of pure mobility in this motion, that mobility which is the link between motion and duration, it passed to the trajectory of the motion, which is pure space; dividing the trajectory into equal parts, it passed from the points of division of this trajectory to the corresponding or "simultaneous" points of division of the trajectory of any other motion. The duration of this last motion was thus measured; we have a definite number of simultaneities; this will be the measure of time; it will henceforth be time itself. But this is time only because we can look back at what we have done. From the simultaneities staking out the continuity of motions, we are always prepared to reascend the motions themselves and, through them, the inner duration that is contemporaneous with them, thus replacing a series of simultaneities of the instant, which we count but which are no longer time, by the simultaneity of flows that leads us back to inner, real duration.

Some will wonder whether it is useful to return to it, and whether science has not, as a matter of fact, corrected a mental imperfection, brushed aside a limitation of our nature, by spreading out "pure duration" in space. These will say: "Time, which is pure duration, is always in the course of flowing; we apprehend only its past and its present, which is already past; the future appears closed to our knowledge, precisely because we believe it open to our action—it is the promise or anticipation of unforeseeable novelty. But the operation by which we convert time into space for the purpose of measuring it informs us implicitly of its content. The measurement of a thing is sometimes the revealer of its nature, and precisely at this point mathematical expression turns out to have a magical property: created by us or risen at our bidding, it does more than we asked of it; for we cannot convert into space the time already elapsed without treating all of time the same way. The act by which we usher the past and present into space spreads out the future there without consulting us. To be sure, this future remains concealed from us by a screen; but now we have it there, all complete, given along with the rest. Indeed, what we called the passing of time was only the steady sliding of the screen and the gradually obtained vision of what lay waiting, globally, in eternity. Let us then take this duration for what it is, for a negation, a barrier to seeing all, steadily pushed back; our acts themselves will no longer seem like a contribution of unforeseeable novelty. They will be part of the universal weave of things, given at one stroke. We do not introduce them into the world; it is the world that introduces them ready-made into us, into our consciousness, as we reach them. Yes, it is we who are passing when we say time passes; it is the motion before our eyes which, moment by moment, actualizes a complete history given virtually." Such is the metaphysic immanent in the spatial representation of time. It is inevitable. Clear or confused, it was always the natural metaphysic of the mind speculating upon becoming. We need not discuss it here, still less replace it by another. We have explained elsewhere why we see in duration the very stuff of our existence and of all things, and why, in our eyes, the universe is a continuity of creation. We thus kept as close as possible to the immediate; we asserted nothing that science could not accept and use; only recently, in an admirable book, a philosopher-mathematician affirmed the need to admit of an "advance of Nature" and linked this conception with ours.[8] For the present, we are confining ourselves to drawing a demarcation line between what is theory, metaphysical construction, and what is purely and simply given in experience; for we wish to keep to experience. Real duration is *experienced;* we *learn* that time unfolds and, moreover, we are unable to measure it without converting it into space and without assuming all we know of it to be unfolded. But, it is impossible mentally to spatialize only a part; the act, once begun, by which we unfold the past and thus abolish real succession involves us in a total unfolding of time; inevitably we are then led to blame human imperfection for our ignorance of a future that is present and to consider duration a pure negation, a "deprivation of eternity." Inevitably we come back to the Platonic theory. But since this conception *must* arise because we have no way of limiting our spatial representation of elapsed time to the past, it is *possible* that the conception is erroneous, and in any case *certain* that it is purely a mental construction. Let us therefore keep to experience.

---

[8] Alfred North Whitehead, *The Concept of Nature* (Cambridge: Cambridge University Press, 1920). This work (which takes the theory of relativity into account) is certainly one of the most profound ever written on the philosophy of nature. [The relevant passage occurs on page 54 of Whitehead's work and reads as follows: "It is an exhibition of the process of nature that each duration happens and passes. The process of nature can also be termed the 'passage of nature.' I definitely refrain at this stage from using the word 'time,' since the measurable time of science and of civilized life generally merely exhibits some aspects of the more fundamental fact of the passage of nature. I believe that in this doctrine I am in full accord with Bergson, though he uses 'time' for the fundamental fact which I call the 'passage of nature.' "]

If time has a positive reality, if the delay of duration at instantaneity represents a certain hesitation or indetermination inherent in a certain part of things which holds all the rest suspended within it; in short, if there is creative evolution, I can very well understand how the portion of time already unfolded may appear as juxtaposition in space and no longer as pure succession; I can also conceive how every part of the universe which is mathematically linked to the present and past—that is, the future unfolding of the inorganic world—may be representable in the same schema (we once demonstrated that in astronomical and physical matters *prevision* is really a *vision*). We believe that a philosophy in which duration is considered real and even active **can** quite readily admit Minkowski's and Einstein's space-time (in which, it must be added, the fourth dimension called time is no longer, as in our examples above, a dimension completely similar to the others). On the other hand, you will never derive the idea of a temporal flow from Minkowski's schema. Is it not better, in that case, to confine ourselves, until further notice, to that one of the two points of view which sacrifices nothing of experience, and therefore—not to prejudge the question—nothing of appearances? Besides, how can a physicist wholly reject inner experience if he operates with perceptions and, therefore, with the data of consciousness? It is true that a certain doctrine accepts the testimony of the senses, that is, of consciousness, in order to obtain terms among which to establish relations, then retains only the relations and regards the terms as nonexistent. But this is a metaphysic grafted upon science, it is not science. And, to tell the truth, it is by abstraction that we distinguish both terms and relations: a continual flow from which we simultaneously derive both terms and relations and which is, over and above all that, fluidity; this is the only immediate datum of experience.

But we must close this overly long parenthesis. We believe we have achieved our purpose, which was to describe the salient features of a time in which there really is succession. Abolish these features and there is no longer succession, but juxtaposition. You can say that you are still dealing with time—we are free to give words any meaning we like, as long as we begin by defining that meaning—but we shall know that we are no longer dealing with an experienced time; we shall be before a symbolic and conventional time, an auxiliary magnitude introduced with a view to calculating real magnitudes. It is perhaps for not having first analyzed our mental view of the time that flows, our feeling of real duration, that there has been so much trouble in determining the philosophical meaning of Einstein's theories, that is, their relation to reality. Those whom the paradoxical appearance of the theories inconvenienced have declared Einstein's multiple times to be purely mathematical entities. But those who would like to dissolve things into relations, who regard every reality, even ours, as a confusedly perceived mathematics, are apt to declare that Minkowski's and Einstein's space-time is reality itself, that all of Einstein's times are equally real, as much and perhaps more so than the time that flows along with us. We are too hasty in both instances. We have just stated, and we shall soon demonstrate in greater detail, why the theory of relativity cannot express all of reality. But it is impossible for it not to express some. For the time that intervenes in the Michelson-Morley experiment is a real time—real again is the time to which we return with the application of the Lorentz formulae. If we leave real time to end with real time, we have perhaps made use of mathematical artifices in between, but these must have some connection with things. It is therefore a question of allotting shares to the real and to the conventional. Our analyses were simply intended to pave the way for this task.

But we have just uttered the word "reality"; and in what follows, we shall constantly be speaking of what is real and not real. What shall we mean by that? If it were necessary to define reality in general, to say by what sign we recognize it, we could not do so without classifying ourselves within a school; philosophers are not in agreement, and the problem has received as many solutions as there are shades of realism and idealism. We would, besides, have to distinguish between the standpoints of philosophy and science; the former rather regards the concrete, all charged with quality, as the real; the latter extracts or abstracts a certain aspect of things and retains only size or relation among sizes. Very happily, we have only to be occupied, in all that follows, with a single reality, time. This being so, it will be easy for us to follow the rule we have imposed upon ourselves in the present essay, that of advancing nothing that cannot be accepted by any philosopher or scientist—even nothing that is not implied in all philosophy and science.

Everyone will surely agree that time is not conceived without a *before* and an *after*—time is succession. Now we have just shown that where there is not some memory, some consciousness, real or virtual, established or imagined, actually present or ideally introduced, there cannot be a before *and* an after; there is one *or* the other, not both; and both are needed to constitute time. Hence, in what follows, whenever we shall wish to know whether we are dealing with a real or an imaginary time, we shall merely have to ask ourselves whether the object before us can or cannot be perceived, whether we can or cannot become conscious of it. The case is privileged; it is even unique. If it is a question of color, for example, consciousness undoubtedly intervenes at the beginning of the study in order to give the physicist the perception of the thing; but the physicist has the right and the duty to substitute for the datum of consciousness something measurable and numerable with which he will henceforward work while granting it the name of the original perception merely for greater convenience. He can do so because, with this original perception eliminated, something remains, or at the very least, is deemed to remain. But what will be left of time if you take succession out of it? And what is left of succession if you remove even the possibility of perceiving a before and an after? I grant you the right to substitute, say, a line for time, since to measure it is quite in order. But a line can be called time only when the juxtaposition it affords is convertible into succession; other-wise you are arbitrarily and conventionally giving that line the name of time. We must be forewarned of this so as not to lay ourselves open to a serious error. What will happen if you introduce into your reasoning and figuring the hypothesis that the thing you called "time" *cannot,* on pain of contra-diction, be perceived by a consciousness, either real or imagi-nary? Will you not then be working, by definition, with an imaginary, unreal time? Now such is the case with the times with which we shall often be dealing in the theory of rela-tivity. We shall meet with perceived or perceptible ones—those will be considered real. But there are others that the theory prohibits, as it were, from being perceived or becoming per-ceptible; if they became so, they would change in scale, so that measurement, correct if it bears upon what we do not perceive, would be false as soon as we do perceive. Why not declare these latter unreal, at least as far as their being "temporal" goes? I admit that the physicist still finds it convenient to call them time; we shall soon see why. But if we liken these times to the other, we fall into paradoxes that have certainly hurt the theory of relativity, even if they have helped popularize it. It will therefore be no surprise if, in the present study, we require the property of being perceived or perceptible for everything held up as real. We shall not be deciding the ques-tion of whether all reality possesses this salient feature. We are only dealing here with the reality of time.

CHAPTER FOUR

Concerning the Plurality of Times

The multiple, slowed times of the theory of relativity: why they are compatible with a single, universal time; "learned" simultaneity, dislocatable into succession: why it is compatible with the natural, "intuitive" simultaneity; examination of the paradoxes of time; the hypothesis of the passenger in a projectile; Minkowski's schema; the confusion that is the source of all the paradoxes

LET US then finally turn to Einstein's time, going back over everything we said when at first we assumed a motionless ether. Here is the earth in motion in its orbit, and, on it, the Michelson-Morley apparatus. The experiment is performed. It is begun again at different times of the year and, consequently, for different speeds of our planet. Always the beam of light behaves as if the earth were motionless. Such is the fact. What is its explanation?

But first, why speak of speeds of our planet? Is then the earth, absolutely speaking, in motion through space? Of course not; we are at the standpoint of relativity and there is no more absolute motion. When you speak of the orbit described by the earth, you are placing yourself at an arbitrarily chosen point of view, that of the inhabitants of the sun (of a sun become habitable). It suits you to adopt this system of reference. But why should the beam of light shot against the mirrors of the apparatus take your whim into account? If all that actually occurs is the reciprocal displacement of the earth and the sun, we can take the sun, the earth, or any other observation post as our system of reference. Let us choose the earth. The problem disappears with regard to it. We need no longer wonder why the interference bands preserve the same appearance, why the same result is observed at any time of the year. Quite simply, it is because the earth is motionless.

It is true that, in our eyes, the problem then reappears with regard to the inhabitants of the sun. I say "in our eyes," because, to a solar physicist, the question will no longer concern the sun; it is now the earth that is moving. In short, each of the two physicists will still pose the problem for the system that is not his.

Each of them will find himself with respect to the other in the situation Peter was in earlier with regard to Paul. Peter was stationed in the motionless ether; he lived in a privileged system S. He saw Paul, borne along in the motion of the moving system S', performing the same experiment as he did and obtaining the same speed for light, even though this speed ought to have been reduced by that of the moving system. The matter was explained by the slowing of time, the contractions in length and the breakup of simultaneity that motion brought about in system S'. Now, no more absolute motion and therefore no more absolute rest: each of the two systems in reciprocal displacement is immobilized in turn by the ruling that gives it the status of a system of reference. But, all the while this convention is maintained, we shall be able to repeat about the immobilized system what was said before about the actually stationary system, and about the mobilized system, what applied to the moving system actually traveling through the ether. In order to fix our ideas, let us again give the titles of S and S' to two systems in mutual displacement. And, to simplify things, let us assume that the whole universe reduces to these two systems. If S is the system of reference, the physicist located in S, bearing in mind that his colleague in S' finds the same speed for light as he, interprets the result as we did above. He reflects: "The system travels at speed v with respect to me, motionless. But, the Michelson-Morley experiment gives the same result over there as here. The truth is, therefore, that, as a result of motion, a contraction takes place in the direction of the system's motion: a length l becomes $l\sqrt{1 - \frac{v^2}{c^2}}$. Moreover, an expansion of time is linked to this contraction of lengths; where a clock in S' ticks off a t' number of seconds, there has really elapsed $\frac{t'}{\sqrt{1 - \frac{v^2}{c^2}}}$ of them. Finally, when the clocks in S', placed at intervals along its direction of motion and separated by distances of l, point to the same time, I see that the signals going and coming between two consecutive clocks do not make the same trip on leaving as on returning, as a physicist inside system S' and unaware of its motion believes; when these clocks show him a simultaneity, they are really pointing to successive moments separated by $\frac{lv}{c^2}$ of his clock's seconds and, therefore by $\frac{lv}{c^2\sqrt{1 - \frac{v^2}{c^2}}}$ seconds of mine."

Such would be the reasoning of the physicist in S. And, building up a unified mathematical representation of the universe, he would make use of the space and time measurements of his colleague in system S' only after having made them undergo the Lorentz transformation.

But the physicist in system S' would proceed in exactly the same way. Ruling himself motionless, he would repeat of S everything that his colleague located in S would have said about S'. In the mathematical representation of the universe which he would build up, he would consider the measurements that he himself would have taken within his own system as being exact and definitive but would correct in accordance with the Lorentz formulae all those which would have been taken by the physicist attached to system S.

Thus, two mathematical representations of the universe would be obtained, completely different from one another if we consider the figures appearing in them, identical if we take into account the relations among phenomena which they indicate—relations that we call the laws of nature. That difference is, moreover, the very condition of this identity. When we take different photographs of an object while walking around it, the variability of the details only expresses the invariability of their interrelations, in other words, the permanence of the object.

Here we are, then, brought round again to multiple times, to simultaneities that are successions, and to successions that are simultaneities, to lengths that must be measured differently according to whether they are ruled stationary or moving. But this time we are before the definitive form of the theory of relativity. We must ask ourselves how these words are to be understood.

Let us first consider the plurality of times, going back to our two systems S and S'. The physicist situated in S adopts his system as the system of reference. There they are, then, S at rest and S' in motion. Inside this system ruled motionless, our physicist begins the Michelson-Morley experiment. To attain our presently limited aim it will be useful to cut the experiment in two and to hold on to only half of it, if we may so express ourselves. We shall therefore assume that the physicist is occupied only with the journey of light in the direction OB perpendicular to that of the reciprocal motion of the two systems. On a clock located at point O, he reads the time t that the beam has taken to go from O to B and back again. What kind of time are we dealing with?

With a real time, of course, in the meaning that we gave above to this expression. Between the beam's departure and return, the physicist's consciousness has lived a certain duration; the motion of the clock hands is a flow contemporaneous with this inner flow and serves to measure it. On this point there is no doubt or difficulty. A time lived and recorded by a consciousness is real by definition.

Let us now consider a second physicist located in S'. He rules himself motionless, being used to taking his own system as the system of reference. There he is, performing the Michelson-Morley experiment or, rather, he too, only half of it. On a clock placed at O', he notes the time that the beam of light takes to go from O' to B' and back again. What, then, is this time that he records? The time that he lives, of course. The motion of his clock is contemporaneous with the flow of his consciousness. It is, again, a real time by definition.

Thus, the time lived and recorded by the first physicist in his system and the time lived and recorded by the second one in his are both real times.

Are they both one and the same time? Are they different times? We are going to demonstrate that we are dealing with the same time in both cases.

Indeed, whatever the meaning we assign to the slowings or accelerations of time, and therefore to the multiple times that are in question in the theory of relativity, one thing is certain: these slowings and accelerations are due only to the motions of the systems we are considering and are subject only to the speed with which we imagine each system propelled. We are therefore changing nothing in any time whatever, real or imaginary, in system S', if we assume that this system is a duplicate of system S; for the system's content, the nature of the events that unfold in it, are extraneous; only the system's speed of translation matters. But if S' is a double of S, it is obvious that the time lived and noted by the second physicist during his experiment in system S', judged motionless by him, is identical with the time lived and noted by the first in system S likewise judged motionless, since S and S', once immobilized, are interchangeable. Hence, the time lived and recorded in the system, the time inside of and immanent in the system, in short, real time, is the same for S and S'.

But what then are the multiple times with their unequal speeds of flow which the theory of relativity finds in different systems in accordance with the speed with which these systems are propelled?

Let us return to our two systems S and S'. If we consider the time which the physicist Peter, situated in S, attributes to system S', we see that this time is, indeed, slower than the time recorded by Peter in his own system. The former time is there-

fore not lived by Peter. But we know that it is not lived by
Paul either. It is therefore not lived either by Peter or Paul.
With even more reason is it not lived by others. But this is
not saying enough. If the time attributed by Peter to Paul's
system is not lived by Peter, Paul, or anyone, is it at least
conceived by Peter as lived or able to be lived by Paul, or,
more generally, by someone, or still more generally by something? Looking closely, we see that it is nothing of the kind.
To be sure, Peter pastes a label on this time with Paul's name
on it; but if he were picturing a conscious Paul, living his own
duration and measuring it, *he would by that very act see Paul
take his own system as system of reference and therefore
take his place within this single time, inside each system, to
which we have just referred; by that very act, moreover, Peter
would also take temporary leave of his system of reference,
consequently, of his existence as a physicist, and consequently,
of his consciousness as well; Peter would no longer see himself
as anything but a vision of Paul's.* But when Peter attributes
a slowed time to Paul's system, he is no longer thinking of
Paul as a physicist, nor even a conscious being. He is emptying
Paul's visual image of its inner, living consciousness, retaining
of the person only its outer envelope (it alone, in fact, is of
interest to physics). Then, Peter takes the figures by which
Paul would have designated the time intervals of his own sys-
tem, were he conscious, and multiplies them by $\dfrac{1}{\sqrt{1-\dfrac{v^2}{c^2}}}$ so as

to make these figures fit into a mathematical representation of
the universe conceived from his own point of view and no
longer from Paul's. Thus, to sum up, whereas the time attributed by Peter to his own system is a time he has lived, the
time he attributes to Paul's is neither a time that either Peter
or Paul has lived, nor a time that Peter conceives as lived or as
capable of being lived by a living, conscious Paul. What is it,
then, if not a mere mathematical expression meant to indicate
that Peter's not Paul's system has been taken as the system
of reference?

I am an artist and I have to portray two subjects, John and James, the one standing next to me and the other, two or three hundred yards away. I draw the former life-size and shrink the latter to the size of a midget. A fellow artist standing next to James and also desirous of painting the two will proceed inversely; he will show John very small and James in normal size. We shall, moreover, both be right. But because we are both right, are we therefore justified in concluding that John and James have neither normal nor a midget's stature, or that they have both at once, or anything we like? Of course not. Shape and size are terms that have an exact meaning in connection with a posed model; it is what we perceive of the height and width of an individual when we are standing next to him, when we can touch him and measure his body with a ruler. Being next to John, measuring him if I like and intending to paint him in his normal height, I grant him his real size; and, in portraying James as a midget, I am simply expressing the impossibility of my touching him—even, if we may be permitted to say so, the degree of this impossibility; the *degree of impossibility* is exactly what is called distance, and it is distance for which perspective makes allowance. In the same way, in the system in which I live and which I mentally immobilize by conceiving as a system of reference, I directly measure a time that is mine and my system's; it is this measurement which I inscribe in my mathematical representation of the universe for all that concerns my system. But in immobilizing my system, I have set the others moving, and I have set them moving variously. They have acquired different speeds. The greater their speed, the further *removed* they are from my immobility. It is this greater or lesser *distance* of their speed from my zero speed which I express in my mathematical representation of other systems when I assign them more or less slowed times, all, of course, slower than mine, just as it is the greater or lesser distance between James and me which I express by shrinking his figure more or less. The multiplicity of times which I thus obtain does not preclude the unity of real time; rather, it presupposes it, in the same way that the diminution of James's figure with distance, on a series of canvases in which I would show him more or less distant, indicates that James remains the same size.

Thus is effaced the paradoxical form given the theory of the plurality of times. "Imagine," we are told, "a passenger in a projectile launched from the earth at about one twenty-thousandth less than the speed of light, which meets a star and returns to the earth at the same speed. Having aged, say, two years up to the time he gets out of his vehicle, he discovers that our globe has aged two hundred years." Are we really sure of this? Let us look more closely. We shall see the mirage effect vanish, for it is nothing else.

The projectile has been fired from a cannon attached to the motionless earth. Let Peter be the one who remains beside the cannon, the earth then becoming our system S. The passenger in the projectile S' then becomes Paul. The theory has been advanced, we said, that Paul would return after two hundred years lived by Peter. Peter has therefore been considered living and conscious; two hundred years of his inner flow have really elapsed for Peter between the departure and return of Paul.

Let us now turn to Paul. We wish to know how much time he has lived. It is therefore to the living, conscious Paul that we must address ourselves and not to Paul's image represented in Peter's consciousness. But the living, conscious Paul obviously takes his vehicle as his system of reference; in that very act, he immobilizes it. As soon as we address ourselves to Paul, we are with him, we adopt his point of view. But then, presto, the projectile has stopped; it is the cannon, with the earth attached, which flies through space. We must now repeat for Paul everything we said about Peter: since motion is reciprocal, the two people are interchangeable. If, earlier, looking into Peter's consciousness, we witnessed a certain flow, we are going to find exactly the same flow in Paul's consciousness. If we said that the first flow lasted two hundred years, the other flow will also last two hundred years. Peter and Paul, earth and projectile, will have gone through the same duration and aged equally.

Where then are the two years of slowed time which were gently to idle by for the projectile while two hunderd years would have to race past on the earth? Has our analysis vaporized them? Not at all! We are going to rediscover them. But we shall no longer be able to lodge anything in them, neither beings nor things; and we shall have to look for another way not to grow old.

Our two people have actually seemed to be living two hundred years at one and the same time because we placed ourselves at both their viewpoints. This was necessary in order to interpret philosophically Einstein's thesis, which is that of the radical relativity and, therefore, the perfect reciprocity of rectilinear, uniform motion.[1] But this procedure is proper to the philosopher who takes Einstein's thesis in its wholeness and attaches himself to the reality—I mean the perceived or perceptible thing—which this thesis plainly expresses. It involves not for a moment losing sight of the idea of reciprocity and, consequently, going unceasingly from Peter to Paul and from Paul to Peter, considering them interchangeable, immobilizing them by turns, immobilizing them, moreover, for only an instant, thanks to a rapid oscillation of the attention that does not wish to give up anything of the thesis of relativity. But the physicist is obliged to proceed otherwise, even if he adheres unreservedly to Einstein's theory. He unquestionably begins by aligning himself with it. He affirms reciprocity. He grants that we have the choice between Peter's and Paul's point of view. But, having granted this, he chooses one of the two, for he cannot refer events in the universe simultaneouly to two systems with different axes. If he puts himself mentally in Peter's place, he will record for Peter the time that Peter records for himself, namely, the time really lived by Peter, and for Paul the time that Peter attributes to him. If he is with Paul, he will record for Paul the time that Paul records for himself,

[1] The motion of the projectile can be considered rectilinear and uniform during both its outbound and inbound journeys. This is all that is required for the validity of the argument just advanced. See Appendix I at the end of this volume, p. 163.

namely, the time that Paul actually lives, and for Peter, the time that Paul confers upon him. But, once again, he will of necessity decide between Peter and Paul. Suppose he chooses Peter. It is in that case really two years, and only two years, that he must record for Paul.

The fact is that Peter and Paul are involved with the same physics. They observe the same relations among phenomena, discover the same laws in nature. But Peter's system is motionless and Paul's is in motion. As long as we are dealing with phenomena in some way attached to the system, that is, so defined by physics that the system is deemed to be carrying them along when it is ruled in motion, the laws of these phenomena must plainly be the same for both Peter and Paul: phenomena in motion, being perceived by Paul who is endowed with the same motion as they, are motionless for him and appear exactly as the analogous phenomena in Peter's system do to Peter. But electromagnetic phenomena arise in such a way that even though the system in which they occur is deemed moving, we can no longer consider them as sharing its motion. And yet the interrelations of these phenomena, their relations with the phenomena carried along in the system's motion are still for Paul what they are for Peter. If the projectile's speed is really what we had assumed, Peter can only express this persistence of relations by crediting Paul with a hundredfold slower time than his own, as we see in the Lorentz equations. Were he to reckon otherwise, he would not put down in his mathematical representation of the world that Paul in motion discovers among all phenomena—including the electromagnetic—the same relations as Peter does at rest. He is thus really implicitly granting that Paul, the referent, could become Paul, the referrer, for why are the relations maintained for Paul, why must they be recorded by Peter for Paul as they appear to Peter, if not because Paul could rule himself motionless by the same right as Peter? But it is a mere consequence of this reciprocity that he notes in this way, not the reciprocity itself. Once again, he becomes the referrer and Paul is only the referent. Since this is the case, Paul's time is a hundred times slower than Peter's. But it is attributed, not lived time. The time lived by Paul would be the time of Paul referring and no longer referent—it would be exactly the time that Peter just found.

We always come back, then, to the same point: there is a single real time, and the others are imaginary. What, indeed, is a real time, if not a time lived or able to be lived? What is an unreal, auxiliary, imaginary time if not one that cannot actually be lived by anything or anyone?

But we see the source of the confusion. We would formulate it as follows: the hypothesis of reciprocity can be expressed mathematically only in that of nonreciprocity, because to express mathematically the freedom of choosing between two systems of axes is actually to choose one of them.[2] The faculty of choosing cannot be read in the choice we make by virtue of it. A system of axes, by the very fact that it has been adopted, becomes a privileged system. In its mathematical use, it is indistinguishable from an absolutely motionless system. That is why unilateral and bilateral relativity are mathematically equivalent, at least in the case at hand. The difference exists here only for the philosopher; it shows up only if we ask ourselves what reality, that is, what perceived or perceptible thing, the two hypotheses imply. The older, that of the privileged system in a state of absolute rest, certainly ends up by positing multiple real times. Peter, really motionless, lives a certain duration; Paul, really in motion, would live a slower duration. But the other, that of reciprocity, implies that the slower duration must be attributed by Peter to Paul or by Paul to Peter depending upon whether Peter or Paul is the referrer or the referent. Their situations are identical; they live one and the same time but attribute differing times to each other and thus imply, in accord with the rules of perspective, that the physics of an imaginary observer in motion must be the same as that of a real observer at rest. Hence, the hypothesis of reciprocity gives us at least

[2] What is, of course, always alone in question is the special theory of relativity.

as much reason for believing in a single time as does common sense; the paradoxical idea of multiple times asserts itself only in the theory of the privileged system. But, once more, we can express ourselves mathematically only in the theory of the privileged system, even when we have begun by granting reciprocity; and the physicist, feeling free of the theory of reciprocity once he has done it homage by freely choosing his system of reference, surrenders it to the philosopher and henceforward expresses himself in the language of the privileged system. Paul will enter the projectile, believing in this physics. He will come to realize on the way that philosophy was right.[3]

What has helped foster the illusion is that the special theory of relativity makes the precise claim of seeking for things a representation independent of the system of reference.[4] It

[3] The theory of the passenger sealed in a projectile, and living only two years while two hundred years roll by on earth was set forth by Langevin in his address to the Congress of Bologna in 1911. It is widely known and quoted. Specifically, it is found in Jean Becquerel's important work, *Le principe de relativité et la théorie de la gravitation* (Paris: Gauthier-Villars et Cie, 1922), p. 52.

Even purely from the standpoint of physics, it raises certain difficulties, because we are here really no longer in special relativity. As soon as speed changes direction, there is acceleration and we are dealing with a problem in general relativity.

But, in any case, the solution given above completely removes the paradox and does away with the problem. See the Appendixes at the end of the volume.

We take this opportunity to say that it was Langevin's address to the Congress of Bologna that first drew our attention to Einstein's ideas. We are aware of what all those interested in the theory of relativity owe to the works and teaching of Langevin.

[Langevin read his paper to the general gathering of the Philosophic Congress of Bologna on April 10, 1911. He later published it as "L'Evolution de l'espace et du temps" in the *Revue de Metaphysique et de Morale,* XIX (1911), 455–466.]

[4] We are here confining ourselves to special relativity because we are concerned only with time. It is undeniable that in general relativity we tend not to choose any system of reference, to proceed as for the construction of an intrinsic geometry without co-ordinate axes, to use only constant elements. All the same, even here, the constancy that we actually consider is generally still that of a relation among elements which are themselves subordinate to the choice of a system of reference.

therefore seems to forbid the physicist to place himself at a particular point of view. But there is an important distinction to be made here. Without doubt, the theoretician of relativity intends to give the laws of nature an expression that keeps its form in any system of reference to which events are referred. But this merely means that, placing himself, like any physicist, at a certain point of view, necessarily adopting a certain system of reference and thus noting down certain magnitudes, he establishes among these magnitudes relations that must be kept invariable among the new magnitudes he encounters should he adopt a new system of reference. It is precisely because his method of inquiry and ways of notation assure him of an equivalence among all the representations of the universe taken from every point of view that he has the absolute right (ill assured in the old physics) to adhere to his personal point of view and to refer everything to his own system of reference.[5] But he is obliged to cling to this system generally. To this system the philosopher as well must therefore cling when he wishes to distinguish the real from the imaginary. The real is that which is measured by a real physicist, and the imaginary, that which is represented in the mind of the real physicist as measured by imaginary physicists. But we shall return to this point in due course. For the moment, let us point out another source of illusion, even less apparent than the first.

The physicist Peter grants as a matter of course (this is only an opinion, for it cannot be proven) that there are other consciousnesses like his, spread across the face of the earth, possibly even at every point in the universe. It therefore makes no difference that Paul, John, and James are in motion with respect to him: he sees them as humans who think and feel as he does. This is because he is a man first and a physicist

---

[5] In his charming little book on the theory of relativity (*The General Principle of Relativity* [London: MacMillan and Co., Ltd., 1920]), H. Wildon Carr maintains that this theory implies an idealist conception of the universe. We would not go that far; but we believe that it would certainly be necessary to orient this physics in an idealist direction if we wished to give it the force of a philosophy.

afterward. But when he thinks of Paul, John, and James as beings like himself, endowed with consciousnesses like his, he really forgets his physics or takes advantage of the license it grants him to speak in daily life like the common run of mortals. As a physicist, he is inside the system in which he makes his measurements and to which he refers everything. Men attached to the same system, and therefore conscious like him, will be physicists like him; they in fact work up, out of the same figures, the same world picture taken from the same point of view; they too are referrers. But the other men will be no more than referents; for the physicist, they can now be nothing but empty puppets. If Peter were to concede them feeling, he would at once lose his own; they would have changed from referents to referrers; they would be physicists and Peter would, in turn, have to become a puppet. This leaving-and-entering of consciousness, it might be added, obviously does not begin until we turn our attention to physics, because it is then clearly necessary to choose a system of reference. Outside of that, the men remain as they are, one group like the other. There is no longer any reason for their not living the same duration and evolving in the same time. The plurality of times looms up at the precise moment when there is no more than one man or group to *live* time. Only that time then becomes real: it is the real time of a moment ago, but cornered by the man or group that has been given the status of physicist. All other men, having become marionettes from that moment on, henceforward evolve in times that the physicist imagines, which can no longer be real time, being neither lived nor able to be lived. Since they are imaginary, we can, of course, imagine as many of them as we like.

What we are now going to add will seem paradoxical, yet it is the plain truth. The idea of a real time common to two systems, identical for S and S', asserts itself with greater force in the hypothesis of the plurality of mathematical times than in the commonly accepted hypothesis of a mathematical time, one and universal. For, in every hypothesis other than that of relativity, S and S' are not strictly interchangeable; they occupy different positions with respect to some privileged system; and even if we have begun by making one a duplicate of the other, we see them immediately differing from one another by the sole fact of not maintaining the same relation to the central system. No matter how much we then attribute the same mathematical time to them, as had always been done before Lorentz and Einstein, it is impossible to demonstrate strictly that observers respectively placed in the two systems live the same inner duration and that the two systems therefore have the same real time; it is, then, even very difficult to define this identity of duration with precision; all we can say is that we see no reason why an observer transferring from one system to another should not react the same way psychologically, live the same inner duration, for supposedly equal parts of the same mathematical, universal time. This is sensible reasoning, to which nothing conclusive is opposed, but it is lacking in rigor and precision. On the other hand, the hypothesis of relativity consists, in essence, of rejecting the privileged system; S and S' must therefore be regarded, while we are considering them, as strictly interchangeable if we have begun by making one the duplicate of the other. But, in that event, the two people in S and S' can be led mentally to coincide, like two equal superimposed shapes; they will have to coincide not only with respect to the different modes of *quantity* but even, if I may so express myself, in respect to *quality*, for their inner lives have become indistinguishable, quite like their measurable features: the two systems steadfastly remain what they were at the moment we propounded them, duplicates of one another, while outside the hypothesis of relativity they were no longer entirely so the moment after, when we left them to their fate. But we shall not labor the point. Let us simply say that the two observers in S and S' live exactly the same duration and that the two systems thus have the same real time.

Is this still the case for every system in the universe? We assigned S' any velocity; we can then repeat for every S'' system what we said about S'; the observer we attach to it will live the same duration in it as in S. At most, it will be objected that the reciprocal displacement of S'' and S is not the same as that of S' and S, and that, consequently, when we immobilize S into a system of reference in the first case, we are not doing strictly the same thing as in the second. The duration of the observer in motionless S, when S' is the system that we are referring to S, would not then necessarily be identical with that of this same observer when the system referred to S is S''; there would be, as it were, different *intensities of immobility* in keeping with the greater or lesser speed of the reciprocal displacement of the two systems before one of them, suddenly elevated to a system of reference, had been mentally immobilized. We do not think anyone wants to go that far. But, even then, we would simply adopt the position we usually take when we parade an imaginary observer across the world, judging it right to attribute the same duration to him everywhere. We mean that we see no reason to believe the opposite; when things look one way, it is up to anyone who calls them illusory to prove them so. Now, the idea of assuming a plurality of mathematical times had never occurred before the theory of relativity; it is therefore to it alone that we would refer in order to cast doubt upon the unity of time. And we have just seen that in the only completely clear and precise case of two systems S and S' moving with respect to one another, the theory of relativity would end by supporting the unity of real time more rigorously than we do ordinarily. It permits defining and almost demonstrating this identity, instead of confining us to the vague and merely plausible assertion with which we are generally content. We conclude that, as far as the universality of real time is concerned, the theory of relativity does not shake the accepted belief and tends rather to strengthen it.

Let us now proceed to the second point, the breakup of simultaneities. But let us first recall in a few words what we said about intuitive simultaneity, the one we could call real and lived. Einstein necessarily acknowledges it, since, through it, he notes the time of an event. We may confer upon simultaneity the most learned of definitions, saying that it is an identity between the readings of clocks synchronized through an exchange of optical signals, and concluding that simultaneity is relative to the synchronizing. It is nonetheless true that we compare clocks in order to determine the time of events; but the simultaneity of an event with the clock reading that gives us its time does not follow from any synchronizing of events with clocks, it is absolute.[6] If it did not exist, if simultaneity were only correspondence between clock readings, if it were not also, and before all else, correspondence between a clock reading and an event, we would not build clocks, or no one would buy them. For we buy them only to find out what time it is. But "to find out what time it is" is to note the simultaneity of an event, of a moment of our life or of the outside world, with a clock reading; it is not, in general, to record a simultaneity between clock readings. Hence, it is impossible for the theoretician of relativity not to acknowledge intuitive simultaneity.[7] He makes use of this simultaneity in the very

[6] It is lacking in precision, to be sure. But when we fix this point through laboratory experiments, when we measure the "delay" caused by the psychological establishment of a simultaneity, it is to intuitive simultaneity that we must still have recourse in order to criticize it. In the final analysis, everything rests upon intuitions of simultaneity and succession.

[7] One may, of course, be tempted to raise the objection that, in principle, there is no simultaneity at a distance, however small the distance, without a synchronizing of clocks. One may reason as follows: "Let us consider your 'intuitive' simultaneity between two events A and B. Either it is a merely approximate simultaneity, the approximation being, moreover, sufficient considering the enormously greater distance separating the events among which you are going to establish a 'learned' simultaneity; or else it is a perfect simultaneity, but in that case, you are, without being aware of it, only ascertaining an identity of readings between the two synchronized microbial clocks of which you spoke earlier, clocks that exist virtually at A and B. If you allege that your microbes posted at A and B have recourse to 'intuitive' simultaneity for the reading of their apparatus, we would repeat our argument by this time imagining submicrobes and submicrobial clocks. In short, the imprecision always diminishing, we would find, in the final reckoning, a system of learned simultaneities independent of intuitive simultaneities; the latter are only confused, approximate, provisory visions of the former." But this argument runs

synchronization of the two clocks through optical signals, and he makes use of it three times, for he must note: (1) the optical signal's moment of departure, (2) the moment of its arrival, (3) that of its return. Now, it is easy to see that the other simultaneity, the one that depends upon a synchronizing of clocks carried out through an exchange of signals is still called simultaneity only because we believe we can convert it into intuitive simultaneity.[8] The one who synchronizes the clocks necessarily takes them to be inside his system; as this system is his system of reference, he deems it motionless. For him, therefore, the signals exchanged between two clocks at a distance from one another make the same trip leaving as returning. Were he to place himself at any point equidistant from the two clocks, and were his eyes sharp enough, he would grasp the readings of the two optically synchronized clocks in one instantaneous intuition and would at that moment see them pointing to the same time. To him learned simultaneity therefore always appears able to be converted into intuitive simultaneity, which is why he calls it simultaneity.

This being granted, let us consider two systems S and S' in motion with respect to one another. Let us first take S as our system of reference. By that very act we immobilize it. Clocks have been synchronized in it, as in every system, through an exchange of optical signals. As in every synchronizing, it has

---

counter to the very principle of the theory of relativity, which is never to assume anything more than has actually been found out and actually ascertained by measurement. It would be to postulate that anterior to our human knowledge, which is in a perpetual becoming, there is a knowledge in full, given in eternity in one piece and mingling with reality itself—we would be limited to acquiring the latter, bit by bit. Such was the ruling idea of Greek metaphysics, an idea revived by modern philosophy and, it must be added, natural to our human understanding. I do not mind our concurring in it, but we must not forget that it is a metaphysic, and a metaphysic based upon principles that have nothing in common with those of relativity.

[8] We showed further back (pp. 55–56) and have just repeated that one cannot make a radical distinction between local simultaneity and simultaneity at a distance. There is always a distance which, however small it may be for us, will appear enormous to a microbe-builder of microscopical clocks.

then been assumed that the exchanged signals made the same trip out and back. Indeed, they really do so, since the system is motionless. If we designate C_m and C_n as the points where the two clocks are, an observer inside the system, choosing any point equidistant from C_m and C_n will be able, if he has sharp enough eyes, to embrace from there, in a single act of instantaneous vision, any two events occurring at points C_m and C_n respectively when these two clocks show the same time. Specifically, he will embrace in this instantaneous perception the two concordant readings on the two clocks—readings that are also themselves events. Every simultaneity indicated by clocks will then be able to be converted into intuitive simultaneity inside the system.

Let us then consider system S'. It is clear that the same will happen for an observer inside this system. This observer takes S' as his system of reference. He therefore renders it motionless. The optical signals by means of which he synchronizes his clocks then make the same trip out and back. Hence, when two of his clocks show the same time, the simultaneity they indicate could be lived and become intuitive.

Thus, there is nothing artificial or conventional in simultaneity whether we apprehend it in one or the other of the two systems.

But let us now see how one of the two observers, the one in S, judges what is happening in S'. For him, the S' system is in motion and, as a consequence, optical signals exchanged between its two clocks do not make the same trip out and back, as an observer attached to the system would believe (except, of course, in the special case of two clocks lying in the same plane perpendicular to the system's direction of motion). Therefore, in his eyes, the synchronizing of the two clocks has been performed in such a way that they give the same reading when there is no simultaneity, but succession. Only, let us remark that he is thus adopting an entirely coventional definition of succession, and therefore of simultaneity as well. He agrees to call successive the concordant readings of clocks that will have been synchronized under the conditions that he perceives in system S'—I mean so synchronized that an observer outside the system does not ascribe the same trip to the optical signal out and back. Why does he not define simultaneity by the agreement between readings on clocks so synchronized that the outward and return journeys are the same for observers inside this system? The answer is that each of the two definitions is valid for each of the two observers and that this is precisely why the same events in system S' can be declared simultaneous or successive, according to whether they are envisaged from the point of view of S or S'. But it is easy to see that one of the two definitions is purely conventional, while the other is not.

To verify this, we are going to come back to a hypothesis that we have already set forth. We shall assume that S' is a duplicate of system S, that the two systems are identical, that the same history unfolds within them. They are in a state of reciprocal movement, completely interchangeable; but one of them is adopted as a system of reference and is from then on deemed motionless; this will be S. The hypothesis that S' is a duplicate of S is not damaging to the generality of our demonstration, since the alleged breakup of simultaneity into succession, and into a succession more or less slow as the movement of the system becomes more or less rapid, depends only upon the system's speed, and not at all upon its content. This granted, it is clear that if events A, B, C, D of system S are simultaneous for the observer in S, the identical events A', B', C', D' of system S' will also be simultaneous for the observer in S'. Now, will these two groups A, B, C, D and A', B', C', D', each formed of events simultaneous for an observer inside the system be additionally simultaneous, that is, perceived as simultaneous by a supreme consciousness capable of instantly sympathizing or telepathically communicating with the two consciousnesses in S and S'? It is obvious that there is no objection to this. Indeed, we can imagine, as just before, that the duplicate S' has broken away from S at a certain moment and is then obliged to return to it. We have demonstrated that the observers inside the two systems will have lived the same total duration. We can therefore divide this duration in both systems into a like number of slices such that each one of them is equal to the corresponding slice in the other system. If the moment M when the simultaneous events *A, B, C, D,* occur is found at the extremity of one of the slices (and this can always be arranged), the moment *M'* when the simultaneous events *A', B', C', D'* occur in system *S'* will be the extremity of the corresponding slice. Situated like *M,* inside an interval of duration whose ends coincide with those of the interval where *M* is found, it will necessarily be simultaneous with *M.* And consequently the two groups of simultaneous events *A, B, C, D* and *A', B', C', D'* will really be simultaneous with each other. We can therefore continue to imagine, as in the past, instantaneous slices of a single time and absolute simultaneities of events.

But, from the viewpoint of physics, the argument we have just advanced will be of no consequence. In physics, the problem is, in effect, posed in the following manner: if *S* is at rest and *S'* in motion, why do experiments on the speed of light, carried out in *S,* give the same result in *S'?* And it is understood that only the physicist in system *S* exists as a physicist— the one in system *S'* is merely imagined. Imagined by whom? Necessarily by the physicist in system *S.* The moment we make *S* our system of reference, it is from there, and from there only, that a scientific world view is thenceforth possible. To keep observers in *S* and in *S'* conscious at one and the same time would be to sanction both systems' being given the status of systems of reference and ruled motionless together; but they have been assumed in a state of reciprocal motion; at least one of the two must therefore be moving. To be sure, we shall leave men in the moving one; but they will have momentarily abdicated their consciousness or, at least, their faculties of observation; they will retain, in the eyes of the single physicist, only the physical side of their person as long as it is a question of physics. From here on, our argument gives way, for it involved the existence of equally real men, similarly conscious, enjoying the same rights in both system *S'* and in system *S.*

It can no longer be a question of more than one group of men—real, conscious physicists—those in the system of reference. The others would indeed be hollow puppets or else they would be only virtual physicists, merely conceived in the mind of the physicist in S. How will the latter picture them? He will imagine them, as before, experimenting with the speed of light, but no longer with a single clock, no longer with a mirror that reflects the beam of light and doubles its journey; there is now a single journey and two clocks respectively located at the points of departure and arrival. He will then have to explain how these imagined physicists would find the same speed for light as he, the real physicist, if this entirely theoretical experiment were to become realizable in practice. Now, as he sees it, light moves at a slower speed for system S' (the conditions of the experiment being those we indicated a while back); but also, since the clocks in S' have been so synchronized as to mark simultaneities where he perceives successions, things will work out in such a way that the real experiment in S and the merely imagined experiment in S' will give the same figure for the speed of light. This is why our observer in S holds to the definition of simultaneity that makes it depend upon the synchronization of clocks. That does not prevent the two systems, S' as well as S, from harboring real, lived simultaneities, not governed by clock synchronizations.

We must therefore make a distinction between two kinds of simultaneity and succession. The first is inside events, a part of their materiality, proceeding from them. The other is merely laid down over them by an observer outside the system. The first says something about the system itself; it is absolute. The second is changeable, relative, imaginary; it turns upon the difference, changing with speed, between this system's immobility for itself and its mobility with respect to another; there is an apparent incurvation from simultaneity into succession. The first simultaneity and the first succession belong to an aggregate of things; the second, to the observer's image of them, obtained in mirrors that distort the more, the greater the speed attributed to the system. The incurvation of simultaneity into succession is, moreover, just what is required for the laws of physics, particularly those of electromagnetism, to be the same for the observer within the system who is located in the absolute, as it were, and the observer outside, whose relation to the system can vary indefinitely.

I am in system S', which is assumed to be motionless. I note intuitive simultaneities there between two spatially separated events, O' and A', having taken up a position equidistant from both. Now, since the system is motionless, a light ray that leaves and returns between points O' and A' makes the same trip out and back; if I then work the synchronizing of the two clocks, respectively located at O' and A', under the assumption that the outward and return passages P and Q are equal, I am in the right. Thus I have two ways of recognizing simultaneity at this point: the one, intuitive, by encompassing what occurs at O' and A' in an act of instantaneous vision; the other, derivative, by consulting the clocks; and the two results agree. I now assume that, nothing of what is happening in system S having changed, P no longer seems equal to A. This is what happens when an observer outside S' perceives this system in motion. Are all the former simultaneities [9] going to become successions for this observer? Yes, by convention, if we agree to translate all the temporal relations of all the events in the system into a language such as makes it necessary to change their expression in accordance with whether P appears equal or unequal to Q. This is what we do in the theory of relativity. I, a relativist physicist, after having been inside the system and perceived P equal to Q, leave it; entering an indefinite number of systems assumed motionless by turns and with respect to which S' would then be found endowed with increasing speeds, I see the inequality between P and Q increasing. I then declare that the events that were simultaneous before are becoming successive, and that their temporal separation is increasing. But we have here only a convention, a necessary convention, it must be added, if I wish to preserve the integrity of physical

[9] Exception is made, of course, of those relating to events located in the same plane perpendicular to the direction of motion.

laws. *For it just so happens that these laws, including those of electromagnetism, have been formulated under the assumption that physical simultaneity and succession are defined by the apparent equality or inequality of the* P *and* Q *journeys.* In stating that succession and simultaneity depend upon one's point of view, we are doing nothing more than giving expression to this assumption, recalling this definition. Are we dealing with *real* simultaneity and succession? We are dealing with reality, if we *agree* to call any convention representative of the real once it has been adopted for the mathematical expression of physical facts. So be it; but then let us no longer speak of time; let us say that we are dealing with a succession and simultaneity that have no connection with duration; for, by virtue of a prior and universally accepted convention, there is no time without a before and an after verified or verifiable by a consciousness that compares one with the other, were this consciousness only an infinitesimal consciousness coextensive with the interval between two infinitely adjacent instants. If you define reality by mathematical convention, you get a conventional reality. But actual reality is what is, or could be, perceived. But, once again, outside of this double journey *PQ* which changes in aspect according to whether the observer is inside or outside the system, everything perceived and perceptible in *S'* remains as it is. This means that it does not matter whether *S'* is considered at rest or in motion—real simultaneity remains real simultaneity; and succession, succession.

When you kept *S'* motionless and consequently placed yourself inside this system, learned simultaneity (the one we deduced from the agreement between optically synchronized clocks) coincided with intuitive or innate simultaneity; *and it is only because it was of use to you in recognizing this innate simultaneity, because it was its token, because it was convertible into intuitive simultaneity, that you called it simultaneity.* Now, *S'* being ruled in motion, the two kinds of simultaneity no longer coincide; all that was innate simultaneity remains innate simultaneity; but the faster the system's speed, the greater grows the inequality between the *P* and *Q* journeys,

although it was by their equality that the learned simultaneity
was defined. What ought you to do if you felt sorry for the
poor philosopher, condemned to a tête-à-tête with reality, acquainted with it alone? You would give another name to the
learned simultaneity, at least when you talk philosophy. You
would invent another word for it, any word, but you would
not call it simultaneity, for it owes this name solely to the
fact that it betokened the presence of a natural, intuitive, real
simultaneity in S' assumed motionless, and that we can now
believe that it still denotes this presence. You yourself, moreover, keep admitting the legitimacy of this original meaning
of the word, at the same time as its primacy; for when S' seems
to you to be in motion, when, speaking of the agreement of its
clocks, you seem no longer to be thinking of learned simultaneity, you keep appealing to the other, the real one, through
your establishment of a "simultaneity" between a clock reading and an "adjacent" event (adjacent for you, a man, but
vastly separated for a discerning microbe-scientist). Nevertheless, you hold on to the word. Indeed, through this word common to both cases and working magically (does not science
act upon us like ancient magic?) you perform a transfusion of
reality from one simultaneity to the other, from innate to
learned simultaneity. The passing from stability to mobility
having doubled the meaning of the word, you slip all the
materiality and solidity of the first meaning into the second.
I would say that instead of forewarning the philosopher against
this error, you want to draw him into it, did I not realize the
advantage you derive, as a physicist, from using the word
simultaneity in both senses: you remind yourself in this way
that learned simultaneity began as innate simultaneity and can
always turn into it again should thought immobilize the
system anew.

From the point of view which we called that of unilateral
relativity, there is an absolute time and an absolute clock-time,
the time and clock-time of the observer located in the privileged system S. Let us assume once more that S', having at first
coincided with S, has then separated from it by way of doubling.

We can say that the clocks in S', which continue to be synchronized in the same way, by optical signals, show the same clock-time when they ought to show different clock-times; they note simultaneity in cases where there is actually succession. If, then, we take the position of unilateral relativity, we shall have to admit that the simultaneities in S break up in its duplicate S' by sole virtue of the motion that causes S' to leave S. To the observer in S' they appear to be retained, but they have become successions. On the other hand, in Einstein's theory, there is no privileged system; the relativity is bilateral; everything is reciprocal; the observer in S is as much in the right in seeing succession in S' as is the observer in S' in seeing simultaneity there. But what are also in question are the successions and simultaneities defined solely by the appearance assumed by the two journeys P and Q. The observer in S' is not mistaken, since, for him, P is equal to Q: the observer in S is no more mistaken, since, for him, the P and Q of system S' are unequal. But, unconsciously, after accepting the theory of double relativity, we revert to that of single relativity, first, because they are mathematically equivalent, then, because it is very difficult not to imagine according to the latter when we think according to the former. We then act as if—the two passages P and Q appearing unequal when the observer is outside S'—the observer inside S' were mistaken in designating these passages as equal, as if events in the physical system S' had been broken up in actuality at the dissociation of the two systems, when it is merely the observer outside S' who rules them broken up in following his own definition of simultaneity. We forget that simultaneity and succession have then become conventional, that they retain of the original simultaneity and succession merely the property of corresponding to the equality or inequality of the two journeys P and Q. It was then still a question of an equality and inequality found by an observer inside the system and therefore final and unchanging.

We shall easily be convinced that the confusing of the two viewpoints is natural and even inevitable, when reading certain pages in Einstein himself. Not that Einstein was obliged to commit this error, but the distinction we have just drawn is of such a nature that the language of the physicist is hardly able to express it. It is, besides, of no importance to the physicist, since the two conceptions are conveyed in the same manner in mathematical terms. But it is the essential point for the philosopher, who will picture time altogether differently according as he takes one position or the other. The pages that Einstein has devoted to the relativity of simultaneity in his book on *The Theory of Special and General Relativity* are instructive in this regard. We quote the heart of his demonstration:

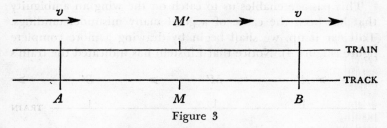

Figure 3

Suppose that an extremely long train moves on its track at a speed *v*, as shown in Figure 3. The passengers on this train will choose to consider it as their system of reference; they will refer every event to the train. Every event that takes place at a point on the track also takes place at a particular point on the train. The definition of simultaneity is the same with respect to the train as with respect to the track. But the following question then arises: are two events (for example two flashes of lightening *A* and *B*) simultaneous with *respect to the track* also simultaneous with respect to the train? We shall straightaway show that the answer is in the negative. In saying that the two flashes of lightning *A* and *B* are simultaneous with respect to the track, this is what we mean: the light rays emitted from points *A* and *B* will meet in the middle *M* of the distance *AB* measured along the track. But to the events *A* and *B* there also correspond points *A* and *B* on the train. Suppose *M'* is the middle of the vector *AB* of the moving train. This point *M'* certainly coincides with point *M* at the instant the flashes of lightning occur (an instant recorded with respect to the track), but it then moves to the right on the diagram at speed *v* of the train.

If an observer at M' on the train were not borne along at this speed, he would remain constantly at M, and the light rays emitted from points A and B would reach him simultaneously, that is, these rays would cross exactly upon him. But, in reality, he is traveling (with respect to the track) and is proceeding toward the light from B, while fleeing the light from A. The observer will therefore see the first sooner than the second. Observers who take the track as their system of reference conclude that the flash of lightning B has occurred before the flash of lightning A. We therefore arrive at the following basic fact. Events simultaneous with respect to the track are no longer so with respect to the train, and vice versa (relativity of simultaneity). Each system of reference has its own time; a time reading has meaning only if we indicate the system of comparison used for the measurement of time.[10]

This passage enables us to catch on the wing an ambiguity that has been the cause of a good many misunderstandings. To clear it up, we shall begin by drawing a more complete figure (Figure 4). Notice that Einstein has indicated the train's

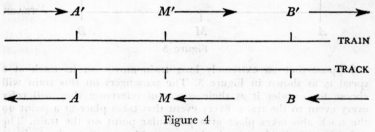

Figure 4

direction by arrows. We shall indicate the opposite direction of the track by other arrows. For we must not forget that the train and the track are in a state of reciprocal motion. To be sure, Einstein does not forget this either when he refrains from drawing arrows along the track; he thereby indicates that he chooses the track as his system of reference. But the philosopher, who wants to know what to believe regarding the nature of time, who wonders whether or not the track and the train have the same real time—that is, the same lived or livable time—the philosopher must always remember that he does not

10 Albert Einstein, *La Théorie de la relativité restreinte et generalisé*, trans. Mle. J. Rouvière (Paris: Gauthier-Villars, 1921), pp. 21, 22.

have to choose between the two systems; he will place a conscious observer in both and will seek out the lived time of each. Let us therefore draw additional arrows. Let us now add two letters, A' and B', to mark the extremities of the train. By not giving them labels of their own, by leaving them with the letters A and B of the points on the earth with which they coincide, we would once again risk forgetting that both track and train are subject to the rule of complete reciprocity, and enjoy equal independence. Finally, we shall more generally call M' any point on the line $A'B'$ which will be located with respect to B' and A' as M is with respect to A and B. So much for the Figure.

Let us now emit our two flashes of lightning. The points from which they set out no more belong to the ground than to the train; the waves advance independently of the motion of their source.

It then becomes evident at once that the two systems are interchangeable, and that exactly the same thing will occur at M' as at the corresponding point M. If M is the middle of AB, and if it is at M that we perceive a simultaneity on the track, it is at M', the middle of $B'A'$, that we shall perceive this same simultaneity in the train.

Accordingly, if we really cling to the perceived, to the lived, if we question a real observer on the train and on the track, we shall find that we are dealing with one and the same time—what is simultaneity with respect to the track is simultaneity with respect to the train.

But, in marking the double set of arrows, we have given up adopting a system of reference; we have mentally placed ourselves on the track and in the train *at one and the same time;* we have refused to turn physicist. We were not, in fact, looking for a mathematical representation of the universe; the latter must naturally be conceived from one point of view and conform to the laws of mathematical perspective. We were asking ourselves what is real, that is, observed and actually recorded.

On the other hand, for the physicist, there is what he himself records—this, he notes as it is—and then there is what he records of another's possible recording; this he will transpose,

lead around to his point of view, since every physical representation of the universe has to be referred to a system of reference. But his notation of it will then no longer correspond to
anything perceived or perceptible; it will therefore no longer
be a notation of the real but of the symbolic. The physicist
located in the train will therefore entertain a mathematical
vision of the universe in which everything will be converted
from perceived reality into useful scientific representation,
except what relates to the train and the objects attached to it.
The physicist on the track will entertain a mathematical vision
of the universe in which everything will be similarly trans-
posed, except what concerns the track and the objects bound
to it. The magnitudes appearing in these two visions will be
generally different, but, in both, certain relations among magnitudes, which we call the laws of nature, will remain the
same, and this identity will precisely express the fact that the
two representations are of one and the same thing, of a
universe independent of our representation.

What then does the physicist located at M see on the track?
He records the simultaneity of the two flashes of lightning. Our
physicist cannot be at point M' also. He can only say that he
ideally sees the recording at M' of a nonsimultaneity between
the two flashes. His mathematical representation of the world
will rest entirely on the fact that his adopted system of reference is tied to the earth. Accordingly, the train moves; accordingly, we cannot grant the simultaneity of the two flashes of
lightning at M'. The truth is that nothing has been recorded
at M' since, for that, a physicist at M' would be needed and the
only physicist in the world is, by hypothesis, at M. There is
nothing more at M' than a certain *notation* carried out by
the observer at M, a notation which is, indeed, that of a nonsimultaneity. *Or, if we prefer, there is a merely imagined physicist at* M', *existing only in the mind of the physicist at* M.
The latter will then write like Einstein, "What is simultaneity
with respect to the track is not so with respect to the train."
And he will be right, if he adds, "since physics is built up
from the point of view of the track." He would, moreover,
still have to add, "What is simultaneity with respect to the

train is not so with respect to the track, since physics is built up from the point of view of the train." And, finally, he would have to say: "A philosophy which assumes the viewpoints of both track and train, which then notes as simultaneity in the train what it notes as simultaneity on the track, no longer stands halfway between perceived reality and scientific construction; it is completely in the real, and is moreover, only completely appropriating Einstein's conception which is that of the reciprocity of motion. But that idea, as complete, is philosophical and no longer physical. To convey it in physicist's language, we must take the position of what we called the hypothesis of unilateral relativity. And as this language asserts itself, we do not perceive that we have for a moment adopted this hypothesis. We then speak of a multiplicity of times that are all on the same plane, all real, therefore, if one of them is real. But the truth is that the latter differs fundamentally from the others. It is real, because it is really lived by the physicist. The others, merely thought of, are auxiliary, mathematical, symbolic."

But, the ambiguity is so difficult to clear up that we cannot attack it from too many angles. Let us therefore consider (Figure 5) three points M', N', P' in system S' so arranged on a straight line marking the direction of the system's motion

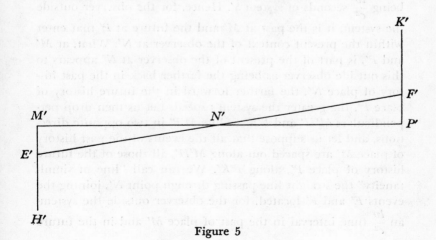

Figure 5

that N' is the same distance l from M' and P'. Let us imagine a person at N'. At each of the three points M', N', P' a series of events unfolds constituting the history of the place. At a particular moment, the person at N' perceives a completely determinate event. But are the events contemporaneous with this one, occurring at N' and P', determinate as well? No, according to the theory of relativity. Depending upon the speed of system S', neither the same event at M' not at P' are contemporaneous with the event at N'. If, then, we regard the present of the person at N' as constituted, at a given moment, by all the simultaneous events that come into being at that moment at all points in his system, only a fragment of it is determinate. This is the event occuring at point N' where the person happens to be. The rest will be indeterminate. The events at M' and P', which are also part of our person's present, will be this or that according as we attribute one speed or another to system S, according as we place him in this or that system of reference. Let us call its speed v. We know that when properly synchronized clocks show the same time at the three points, and consequently, when there is simultaneity in system S', the observer in the S system of reference sees the clock at M' move ahead of and the clock at P' lag behind the one at N', both lead and lag being $\frac{lv}{c^2}$ seconds of system S'. Hence, for the observer outside the system, it is the past at P' and the future at P' that enter within the present context of the observer at N'. What, at M' and P', is part of the present of the observer at N' appears to this outside observer as being the farther back in the past history of place N', the farther forward in the future history of place P', the greater the system's speed. Let us then drop perpendiculars $M'H'$ and $P'K'$ to line $M'P'$ in two opposite directions, and let us suppose that all the events of the past history of place M' are spaced out along $M'H'$, all those of the future history of place P', along $P'K'$. We can call "line of simultaneity" the straight line passing through point N', joining the events E' and F' located, for the observer outside the system, an $\frac{lv}{c^2}$ time interval in the past of place M' and in the future of place P' (the number $\dfrac{lv}{c^2}$ designating seconds in system S').

This line, we see, keeps diverging from $M'N'P'$ as the speed of the system increases.

Here again the theory of relativity takes on, at first glance, a paradoxical appearance, striking the imagination. At once the idea comes to mind that if the gaze of our person at N' could instantly leap the space that separates him from P', he would perceive there a part of the future of that place, since it exists there, since it is a moment of that future which is simultaneous with this man's present. He would thus predict for an inhabitant of place P' events that the latter will witness. "To be sure," we tell ourselves, "instantaneous vision at a distance is not possible in actual fact; there is no speed greater than that of light. But an instantaneity of vision can be imagined, and that is enough for the interval $\dfrac{lv}{c^2}$ of the future of place P' rightfully to pre-exist in its present, to be preformed there and consequently predetermined." We shall see that this is a mirage. Unfortunately, the theoreticians of relativity have done nothing to dispel it. They have, on the contrary, seen fit to intensify it. The moment has not yet come for analyzing Minkowski's conception of space-time, adopted by Einstein. It has been expressed in a very ingenious schema into which, if we were not on our guard, we would risk reading what we have just pointed out, into which, indeed, Minkowski himself and his followers have actually read it. Without as yet applying ourselves to this schema (it would call for a whole series of explanations which we may bypass for the moment), let us convey Minkowski's thought, using the simple figure we just drew.

If we examine $E'N'F'$, our line of simultaneity, we see that, at first merged with $M'N'P'$, it gradually diverges as the speed v of system S' increases with respect to the system of reference S. But it will not diverge indefinitely. We know, in fact, that there is no speed greater than that of light. Hence, the distances $M'E'$ and $P'F'$, equal to $\dfrac{lv}{c^2}$, cannot exceed $\dfrac{l}{c}$. Let us grant

them this length. We shall have, we are told, beyond E' in
the direction of $E'H'$, a region of *absolute past,* and beyond
F' in the direction $F'K'$, a region of *absolute future;* nothing
of this past or future can be a part of the present of the observer at N'. But, in return, none of the moments in interval
$M'E'$ or $P'F'$ is either absolutely before or after the one passing at N'; all these successive moments of the past and future
will be contemporaneous with the event at N', if we like; it
will suffice to attribute the appropriate speed to system S',
that is, in consequence, to choose the system of reference. Anything that has occurred at M' in an elapsed interval $\dfrac{l}{c}$, anything that will take place at P' in an interval $\dfrac{l}{c}$ yet to elapse
can enter the partly indeterminate present of the observer at
N'—the speed of the system will decide what will enter.

The theoreticians of relativity, it must be added, have implicitly admitted that, if the observer at N' had the gift of
instantaneous vision at a distance, he would perceive as present at P' what is going to happen there, since they have taken
care to reassure us about the consequences of such a state of af-
fairs.[11] In actual fact, they point out, the observer at N' will
never make use of this immanence, in his present, of what is
in the past at M' for the observer at M' or of what is in the
future at P' for the observer at P'; never will he profit from
it or cause the inhabitants of M' and P' to rue it; for no mes-
sage can be transmitted, no causality exercised, at a speed
greater than that of light; so that the person at N' could neither be informed of a future of P' that is nevertheless a part
of his present, nor influence the future in any way; that future
can with impunity be included in the present of the person
at N'; practically, it remains nonexistent for him.

11 On this subject, see P. Langevin, "Le temps, l'espace et la causalité,"
Bulletin de la Société française de philosophie (1912); and Sir Arthur
Stanley Eddington, *Espace, temps et gravitation* (*Space, Time, and Gravi-
tation*), trans. J. Rossignol (Paris: J. Hermann, 1921), pp. 61–66.

Let us see if this is not a mirage. We shall return to a supposition which we have already made. According to the theory of relativity, the temporal relations among events unfolding in a system depend solely upon the speed of that system, not upon the nature of those events. The relations will therefore remain the same if we make S' a double of S, unfolding the same history as S and having begun by coinciding with it. This assumption will greatly facilitate matters, and it will in no way detract from the generality of our demonstration.

Accordingly, there is in system S a line MNP from which the line $M'N'P'$ has parted by way of doubling, at the moment S' split from S. By hypothesis, an observer located at M' and one at M, being at two corresponding places in two identical systems, each witnesses the same history of the place, the same march of events. The same holds for the two observers at N and N' and for those at P and P', as long as each of them considers only the place where he is. With this everyone agrees. Now, we are going to pay particular attention to the two observers at N and N', since what is in question is the simultaneity with what is happening at these midpoints.[12]

For the observer at N, that which at M and P is simultaneous with his present is fully determinate, since the system is motionless by hypothesis.

As for the observer at N', that which at M' and P' was simultaneous in his present, when his system S' coincided with S,

[12] To simplify the argument, we shall assume in all that follows that the same event is in the act of being performed at points N and N' in the twin systems S and S'. In other words, we shall look at N and N' at the precise instant of the dissociation of the two systems, allowing system S' to acquire its speed v instantly, in a sudden spurt, without passing through intermediate speeds. Upon this event constituting the common present of the two people at N and N', we then fix our attention. When we shall state that we are increasing speed v, we shall mean that we are putting things back in place, making the two systems coincide again, that, consequently, we are having the persons at N and N' witness the same event, and that we are then dissociating the two systems by imparting to S', again instantly, a speed greater than the one before.

was equally determinate. They were the same two events which, at M and P, were simultaneous in the present of N.

S' now shifts with respect to S and acquires increasing speeds. But for the observer at N', inside S', this system is motionless. The two systems S and S' are in a state of complete reciprocity; it is for the convenience of study, to erect a physics, that we have immobilized one or the other into a system of reference. All that a real, flesh-and-blood observer observes at N, all that he would instantaneously, telepathically observe at no matter how remote a point in his system would be identically perceived by a real flesh-and-blood observer located at N' in S'. Hence, that portion of the history of places M' and P' which really enters the present of the observer at N' *for him*, what he would perceive at M' and P' if he had the gift of instantaneous vision at a distance, is determinate and unchanging, whatever the speed of S' in the eyes of the observer inside system S. It is the same portion that the observer at N would perceive at M and P.

Let us add that the clocks of S' run for the observer at N' absolutely like those of S for the observer at N, since S and S' are in a state of reciprocal motion and, consequently, are interchangeable. When the clocks located at M, N, P, and which are optically synchronized, show the same time and when there is then, by relativist definition, simultaneity among the events occurring at these points, the same is true for the corresponding clocks in S'; and there is then, still by definition, simultaneity among the events occurring at M', N', P'— events respectively identical with the former ones.

But, as soon as I have immobilized S into a system of reference, here is what happens. In system S turned motionless, whose clocks we had optically synchronized, as we always do under the assumption of the system's immobility, simultaneity is something *absolute;* I mean that its clocks having been synchronized by observers necessarily in the system, on the assumption that optical signals between two points N and P make the same trip out and back, this assumption becomes

definitive, is consolidated by the fact that S has been chosen
as system of reference and definitively immobilized.

But, by that very fact, S' is in motion; and the observer in
S then notices that the optical signals between the two clocks
at N' and P' (which the observer in S' supposed and still supposes to be making the same trip out and back) now cover
unequal distances, the inequality growing with every increase
in the speed of S'. By virtue of his definition, then (for we are
assuming the observer in S to be a relativist), the clocks that
show the same time in system S' do not, *in his eyes,* underline
contemporaneous events. There certainly are events that are
contemporaneous for him in his system, as also there are
events that are contemporaneous for the observer at N' in his
own system. But to the observer at N they appear as successive
in system S', or rather, *they appear as having to be noted down
as successive,* by reason of his definition of simultaneity.

Then, as the speed of S' increases, the observer at N drives
farther into the past of point M' and projects farther into the
future of point P'—by the numbers he assigns them—events,
occurring at these points, which are contemporaneous both
for him in his own system and also for an observer located
in system S'. For this last observer, it must be added, there is
no further question of a flesh-and-blood existence; he has been
surreptitiously drained of his content, in any case, of his consciousness; from observer he has become simply observed,
since it is the observer in N who has been given the status
of physicist-builder of all science. Consequently, I repeat, as
v increases, our physicist *notes* as pushed back ever farther
into the past of place M', advanced ever more into the future
of place P', the always identical event which, whether it be
at M' or P', is part of the really conscious present of an observer at N', and consequently part of his own. There are not,
therefore, different events at place P' which enter by turns, for
increasing speeds of the system, into the real present of the
observer at N'. But the same event of place P', which is part
of the present of the observer at N', under the assumption of
the system's immobility, is noted by the observer at N as be-

longing to a future ever more remote from the observer at
N', as the speed of the mobilized system S' increases. If the
observer at N did not so note, it must be added, his physical
conception of the universe would become incoherent, for his
written measurements of phenomena occurring in a system
would express laws that he would have to vary with the system's speed; thus, a system identical with his, whose every
point would have identically the same history as the corresponding point in his, would not be governed by the same
physics (at least in what concerns electromagnetism). But
then, in noting as he does, he is only expressing his need,
when he imagines his stationary system S moving under the
name of S', to *incurvate* the simultaneity among events. It is
always the same simultaneity; it would appear such to an
observer inside S'. But, expressed perspectively from point N,
it must be bent back in the form of succession.

Hence, there is really no need to reassure us, to tell us that
the observer at N' can unquestionably retain part of the future of place P' within his present, but that he can neither
grasp it nor give any idea of it, and that, consequently, this
future is as if nonexistent for him. We are quite undisturbed;
we cannot stuff and reanimate our observer at N' drained of
his content, remake him into a conscious being, a physicist at
that, without the event of place P', which we just shelved in
the future, again becoming the present of this place. Basically,
it is himself whom the physicist at N needs to reassure at this
point, and it is himself whom he reassures. He has to prove
to himself that in numbering the event of point P' as he does,
in locating it in the future of this point and in the present of
the observer at N', he is not only satisfying the requirements
of science, but also remaining fully in accord with ordinary
experience. And he has no trouble in proving this to himself,
because when he represents everything according to the rules
of perspective that he has adopted, what is coherent in reality
continues to be so in the mental view. The same reason that
leads him to believe that there is no speed greater than that of
light, that the speed of light is the same for every observer,

etc., obliges him to shelve in the future of place P' an event that is part of the present of the observer at N', which is, moreover, a part of his own N observer's present, and which belongs to the present of place P. Strictly speaking, he ought to express himself as follows, "I locate the event in the future of place P', but since I leave it within the interval of future time $\frac{l}{c}$, since I do not push it further back, I shall never have to imagine the person at N' as able to perceive what will occur at P' and to inform its inhabitants of it." But the way he sees things makes him say, "In vain does the observer at N' possess something of the future of place P' in his present; he cannot study it, influence it, or use it in any way." Certainly, no physical or mathematical error will result from this statement; but great would be the delusion of the philosopher who would take the physicist at his word.

For the observer at N', therefore, there is not, at M' and P', next to events that we consent to leave in the "absolute past" or in the "absolute future," a whole mass of events which, past and future at those two points, enter his present whenever we attribute the appropriate speed to system S'. There is, at each of these points, only one event making up a part of the *real* present of the observer at N', whatever the speed of the system; it is the very one that, at M and P, is part of the present of the observer at N. But this event will be noted down by the physicist as located more or less back in the past of M', more or less forward in the future of P', according to the speed attributed to the system. It is always, at M' and P', the same couple of events that form together with a certain event at N' the present of Paul located at this latter point. But this simultaneity of three events appears incurvated into past-present-future when beheld in the mirror of motion by Peter picturing Paul.

However, the illusion involved in the current interpretation is so difficult to unmask that it will not be without profit to attack it from still another direction. Let us imagine anew that system S', identical with system S, has just broken away from it and instantly attained its speed. Peter and Paul have been merged at point N; here they are, at the same instant, separate at N and N', which still coincide. Let us now imagine that Peter, in his system S, has the gift of instantaneous vision at a distance. If the motion imparted to system S' really rendered an event in the future of place P' simultaneous with what is occurring at N' (and, consequently, with what is occurring at N, since the dissociation of the two systems takes place at the same instant), Peter would witness a future event of place P, an event that will not, as before, enter the present of the aforesaid Peter; in short, through the intermediary of system S', he would read the future of his own system S, not certainly for point N where he is, but for a distant point P. And the greater the abruptly attained speed of S' the farther will his gaze bore into the future of point P. Had he the means for instantaneous communication, he would announce to an inhabitant of place P what was going to happen at that point, having seen it at P'. But hold on! *What he perceives at* P', *in the future of place* P', *is exactly what he perceives at* P, *in the present of place* P. *The greater the speed of system* S', *the farther back in the future of place* P' *is what he perceives at* P', *but it is ever and anon the same present of point* P. *Vision at a distance, and into the future, does not therefore inform him of anything.* There is no room for anything in "the interval of time" between the present of place P and the future, identical with this present, of the corresponding place P'; everything happens as if the interval were nothing. And it is, in fact, nothing; it has been expanded out of nothing. But it takes on the appearance of an interval through a phenomenon of mental optics, analogous to that which separates an object from itself, as it were, when a pressure on the eyeball makes us see it double. More precisely, the view of system S' which Peter has entertained is nothing other than that of system S "skewed" in time. This "skewed vision" makes the line of simultaneity passing through points M, N, P in system S appear the more oblique in system S', duplicate of S, the greater the speed of system S'; the duplicate of what is occurring at M thus finds itself pushed back into the past, the duplicate of what is occurring at P, pulled forward into the future; but the long and short of it is that we have here only an effect of mental torsion. Now, what we say of system S', duplicate of S, is true of any other system having the same speed; for, once more, the temporal relations of events in S' are affected, following the theory of relativity, by the system's speed, and by its speed only. Let us then imagine that S' is any system and no longer the double of S. If we want to find the exact meaning of the theory of relativity, we must first have S' at rest together with S without merging with it, then have it move. We shall find that what was simultaneity at rest remains simultaneity in motion, but that this simultaneity, perceived from system S, has simply been skewed; the line of simultaneity between the three points M', N', P' appears turned about N' by a certain angle, so that one of its extremities lags behind in the past while the other encroaches upon the future.

We have dwelled upon the "slowing of time" and the "breakup of simultaneity." There remains the "longitudinal contraction." We shall presently show how it is but the spatial manifestation of this double temporal effect. But we can say something about it even now. Let there be (Figure 6) two

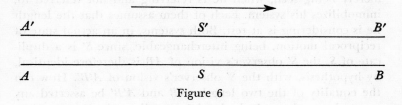

Figure 6

points A' and B' in the moving system S' which, during its journey, happen to settle over two points A and B in the motionless system S, of which S' is the duplicate. When these two coincidings take place, the clocks at A' and B', synchronized, of course, by observers attached to S', show the same time. The observer, attached to S who believes that, in such a case, the clock at B' lags behind the one at A', will conclude that B' coincided with B only after the moment of the coinciding of A' with A, and that, as a consequence, $A'B'$ is shorter than AB. Actually, he "knows" this only in the following sense. In order to conform to the rules of perspective, which we stated earlier, he had to attribute a delay to the coinciding of B' with B over the coinciding of A' with A, precisely because the clocks at A' and B' showed the same time for the two coincidings. Consequently, on pain of contradiction, he has to mark off a shorter length for $A'B'$ than for AB. Moreover, the observer in S' will argue symmetrically. His system is motionless for him; and, consequently, S moves for him in an opposite direction from the one S' just followed. The clock at A therefore appears to him to be lagging behind the clock at B. And, as a result, the coinciding of A with A' will have been effected, according to him, only after that of B with B', if clocks A and B showed the same time at the two coincidings. From which it follows that AB must be shorter than $A'B'$. Now, have AB and $A'B'$ *really* the same length, or have they not? Let us repeat once more that we are here calling real what is perceived or perceptible. We must therefore turn to the observer in S and S', Peter and Paul, and compare their respective perceptions of the two lengths. Now, each of them, when he sees instead of merely being seen, when he is referring and not referred to, immobilizes his system. Each of them assumes that the length he is considering is at rest. Both systems, in an actual state of reciprocal motion, being interchangeable, since S' is a duplicate of S, the S' observer's vision of AB is therefore identical, by hypothesis, with the S' observer's vision of $A'B'$. How can the equality of the two lengths AB and $A'B'$ be asserted any more rigorously and absolutely? Equality takes on an absolute meaning, beyond any convention of measurement, only in the case where the two terms compared are identical; and we declare them identical when we assume them interchangeable. Hence, in the thesis of special relativity, the extended can no more really contract than time slow down or simultaneity actually break up. But, when a system of reference has been adopted and thereby immobilized, everything happening in other systems must be expressed perspectively, according to the greater or lesser difference that exists, on a size-scale, between the speed of the system referred to and the speed, zero by hypothesis, of the referrer system. Let us not lose sight of this distinction. If we have a living John and James step out of the painting where the one occupies the foreground and the other the background, let us be careful not to leave James a midget. Let us give him, like John, his normal size.

To sum it all up, we have only to return to our initial hypothesis of the physicist attached to the earth, repeatedly performing the Michelson-Morley experiment. But we shall now imagine him preoccupied above all with what we are calling real, that is, with what he perceives or can perceive. He remains the physicist, not losing sight of the need to obtain a coherent mathematical representation of the whole. But he wants to help the philosopher in his task; and his gaze never leaves the moving line of demarcation that separates the symbolic from the real, the conceived from the perceived. He will then speak of "reality" and "appearance," of "true measurements" and "false measurements." In short, he will not adopt the language of relativity. But he will accept its theory. The translation of the new idea into the old language with which he will furnish us will make clearer what we can keep and what we ought to change of what we had previously accepted.

Accordingly, revolving his apparatus 90°, at no time of the year does he observe any shift in the interference bands. The speed of light is thus the same in every direction, the same for every speed of the earth. How explain this fact?

"The fact is fully explained," our physicist will declare. "There is no difficulty, a problem is raised only because we speak of an earth in motion. But in motion with respect to what? Where is the fixed point that it approaches and moves away from? This point can have been only arbitrarily chosen. I am then free to decree that the earth shall be this point, and to refer it to itself, as it were. There it is, motionless, and the problem disappears.

Nevertheless, I have one misgiving. How embarrassing if the concept of absolute immobility did take on meaning all the same, a definitively fixed landmark having somewhere come to light? Without even going that far, I have only to look at the stars to see bodies moving with respect to the earth. The physicist attached to one of these extraterrestrial systems, reasoning as I do, will consider himself motionless in turn and rightly so; he will then make the same demands of me as would the inhabitants of an absolutely motionless system. He will tell me, as they would have, that I am deceiving myself, that I have no right to explain the equal speed of propagation of light in every direction by my immobility, for I am in motion.

But here then is how I reassure myself. No extraterrestrial onlooker will ever reproach me, ever catch me in error, because, examining my units of measurement for space and time, observing the moving of my instruments and the rate of my clocks, he will note the following: (1) I undoubtedly attribute the same speed to light as he does, even though I am moving in the direction of the beam of light and he is motionless; but this is because my units of time then appear to him longer than his own; (2) I believe I have established that light is propagated with the same speed in every direction; but this is because I am measuring distances with a ruler whose length he sees changing with its orientation; (3) do I always find that light has the same speed, even if I happen to measure it between two points of its journey on the earth by noting on clocks respectively located at these two places the time it takes to traverse the interval? but this is because my two clocks have been synchronized under the assumption that the earth was motionless. As it is in motion, one of the clocks happens to lag behind the other with every increase in the earth's speed. This slowing will always lead me to think that the time taken by light to traverse the interval is one that corresponds to an ever constant speed. Hence, I am covered. My critic will find my conclusions sound although, from his point of view, which is now alone legitimate, my premises have become false. At most, he will reproach me for believing that I have actually established the constancy of the speed of light in every direction; according to him, I assert this constancy only because my mistakes in measuring time and space so compensate each other as to give a result like his. Naturally, in the representation of the universe that he will build up, he will have my time and space lengths appear as he has just recorded them and not as I had recorded them myself. I shall have been judged to have mistaken my measurements throughout. But no matter, since my result is admitted to be correct. Besides, if the observer merely imagined by me became real, he would find himself confronted by the same difficulty, would have the same misgivings, and would reassure himself in the same way. He would say that, moving or motionless, measuring truly or falsely, he gets the same physics as I do and ends up with universal laws."

In still other terms: given an experiment such as that of Michelson and Morley, things happen as if the theoretician of relativity were pressing one of the experimenter's eyeballs and thus causing a special kind of diplopia; the image first perceived, the experiment first begun, doubles into a phantasmal image where duration slows down, where simultaneity incurvates into succession, and where, for that very reason, lengths change. This diplopia, artificially induced in the experimenter, is to reassure him, or rather, to secure him against the risk he thinks he is running (which he really would be running in certain cases) in arbitrarily making himself the center of the world, in referring everything to his personal system of reference, and in nevertheless building up a physics that he would like to be universally valid. He can rest easy from now on; he knows that the laws he formulates will be confirmed, no matter from what vantage point we view nature. For the phantasmal image of his experiment, an image which shows him how this experiment would look, if the experimental device were in motion, to a motionless observer provided with a new system of reference, is no doubt a temporal and spatial distortion of the first image, but a distortion that leaves the relations among the parts of the framework intact, keeps its connections just as they are, and lets the experiment go on confirming the same law, these connections and relations being precisely what we call the laws of nature.

But our terrestrial observer must never lose sight that, in all this, he alone is real, and the other observer, phantasmal. He may, moreover, evoke as many of these phantasms as he likes, as many as there are speeds, an infinity of them. All will appear to him as building up their representation of the universe, changing the measurements he has taken on earth, obtaining for that very reason a physics identical with his. From then on, he will work away at his physics while remaining unreservedly in his chosen observation post, the earth, and will pay them no more heed.

It was nonetheless necessary that these phantasmal physicists be evoked; and the theory of relativity, by furnishing the real physicist the means for finding himself in agreement with them, has caused science to take a great step forward.

We have just located ourselves on the earth. But we could just as easily have chosen any other point in the universe. At each of these there is a real physicist drawing a host of phantasmal physicists in his wake, as many as the speeds he imagines. Do we wish, then, to sort out the real? Do we want to know whether there is a single time or multiple times? We must pay no attention to phantasmal physicists, we must take account only of real physicists. We shall ask ourselves whether or not they perceive the same time. Now, it is in general difficult for the philosopher to declare with certainty that two people live the same rhythm of duration. He cannot even give this statement a rigorous, precise meaning. Yet he can do so in the hypothesis of relativity. Here the statement takes on a very clear meaning and becomes certain when we compare two systems in a state of reciprocal and uniform motion; the observers are interchangeable. That, indeed, is completely clear and certain only in the hypothesis of relativity. Anywhere else, two systems, however similar, usually differ in some way, since they do not occupy the same place with respect to the privileged system. But the doing away with the privileged system is the very core of the theory of relativity. Hence, this theory, far from ruling out the hypothesis of a single time, calls for it and gives it a greater intelligibility.

CHAPTER FIVE

The Light-Figures

"Light-lines" and rigid-lines—the "light-figure" and the
space-figure; how they coincide and dissociate; triple
effect of the dissociation; (1) transverse effect or "expansion of time," (2) longitudinal effect or "breakup
of simultaneity," (3) transverse-longitudinal effect or
"Lorentz contraction"; true nature of Einstein's time;
transition to the theory of space-time

THIS WAY of looking at things will allow us to penetrate further into the theory of relativity. We have just shown how
the theoretician of relativity evokes, in addition to his perception of his own system, all the mental views ascribable to
all the physicists perceiving that system in motion at every
possible speed. These mental views vary, but the different
parts of each of them are so articulated as to maintain, inside
of each, the same relations among them and thus to manifest
the same laws. Let us now look more closely at these different
mental views. Let us demonstrate, in more concrete fashion,
the increasing distortion of the surface image and the unchanging preservation of its inner relations as the speed is
adjudged increasing. We shall thus catch, as if on the wing,
the genesis of the plurality of times in the theory of relativity.
We shall see its meaning taking physical shape before our eyes.
And, at the same time, we shall extricate certain postulates
which this theory implies.

Here then is the Michelson-Morley experiment (Figure 7)

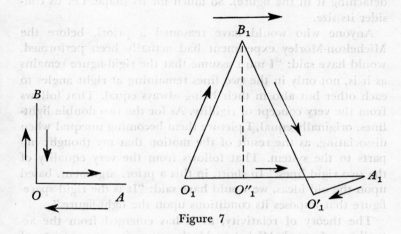

Figure 7

in a motionless system *S*. Let us give the name, "rigid-line," or "line" for short, to a mathematical line such as *OA* or *OB*. Let us call the beam of light that travels over it "light-line." For the observer inside the system, the two beams, both emitted at right angles from *O* to *B* and *O* to *A*, respectively, return exactly upon themselves. The experiment therefore offers him the image of a double light-line stretched between *O* and *B* and *O* and *A*, these two double light-lines being equal and perpendicular to each other.

Now *watching* the system at rest, *imagine* it moving at speed *v*. What will be our double mental view of it?

As long as it is at rest, we can consider it, indifferently, as formed either by two single rigid-lines at right angles or by two double light-lines, again at right angles; the light-figure and rigid-figure coincide. As soon as we imagine it in motion, the two figures dissociate. The rigid-figure stays composed of two lines at right angles. But the light-figure becomes distorted. The double light-line stretched along *OB* becomes a broken light-line $O_1B_1O'_1$. The double light-line stretched along *OA* becomes the light-line $O_1A_1O'_1$ (the portion O'_1A_1 of this line really lies on *O'A'* but, for greater clarity, we are detaching it in the figure). So much for its shape. Let us consider its size.

Anyone who would have reasoned a priori, before the Michelson-Morley experiment had actually been performed, would have said: "I must assume that the rigid-figure remains as it is, not only in the two lines remaining at right angles to each other but also in their being always equal. That follows from the very concept of rigidity. As for the two double light-lines, originally equal, I picture them becoming unequal when dissociating, as the result of the motion that my thought imparts to the system. That follows from the very equality of the two rigid lines." In short, in this a priori argument, based upon the old ideas, we would have said: "It is the rigid space-figure that imposes its conditions upon the light-figure."

The theory of relativity, as it has emerged from the actually performed Michelson-Morley experiment, consists of reversing this proposition and saying, "It is the light-figure that imposes its conditions upon the rigid-figure." In other words, the rigid-figure is not reality itself but only a mental construct; and for this construct it is the light-figure, the sole datum, which must supply the rules.

The Michelson-Morley experiment apprises us, in effect, that the two lines $O_1B_1O'_1$, $O_1A_1O'_1$ remain equal, no matter what speed is attributed to the system. It is therefore the equality of the two double light-lines that will always be considered preserved and not that of the two rigid lines; it is for the latter to arrange themselves accordingly. Let us see how they do this. To that end, let us closely examine the distortion of our light-figure. But let us not forget that everything is happening in our imagination, or, rather, in our understanding. In point of fact, the Michelson-Morley experiment has been performed by a physicist in his system, and, therefore, in a motionless system. The system is in motion only if the physicist mentally leaves it. If he remains there in thought, his argument will not apply to his own system, but to the Michelson-Morley experiment undertaken in another system, or, rather, to the image he forms, which he must form, of this experiment started elsewhere; for, where the experiment is actually performed, it is as yet done by a physicist within the system, and, therefore, in a still motionless one. The result is that, in all this, it is only a question of adopting a certain notation for the experiment we do not perform, in order to co-ordinate it with the one we do perform. We are thus simply saying that we are not performing it. Never losing sight of this point, let us follow the change in our light-figure. We shall separately examine the three distortional effects produced by motion: (1) the transverse effect, which corresponds, as we shall see, to what the theory of relativity calls a lengthening of time; (2) the longitudinal effect, which, for it, is a breaking up of simultaneity; (3) the twofold transverse-longitudinal effect, which is "the Lorentz contraction."

1. THE TRANSVERSE EFFECT OR "EXPANSION OF TIME"

Let us give speed v increasing rates from zero up. Let us train ourselves mentally to turn out of the original light-figure OAB a series of figures in which the divergence between light-lines that first coincided becomes ever more marked. Let us also practice making all those which have thus come out of it retreat within the original figure. In other words, let us proceed as with a spyglass whose tubes we pull out and then telescope. Or better, let us think of that child's toy made of jointed sticks lined with wooden soldiers. When we spread the sticks apart by pulling on the two end ones, they cross like X's and the soldiers break ranks; when we push them back, all the sticks come together and the soldiers close ranks. Let us clearly repeat that the number of our light-figures is infinite and that they are nevertheless but one; their multiplicity merely expresses the possible visions had of them by observers to whom they seem to be traveling at different speeds, that is, the visions that observers moving relative to them have; and all these virtual visions telescope, so to speak, into the real vision of the original figure AOB. What conclusion forces itself upon us regarding the transverse light-line $O_1B_1O'_1$, the one which has sprung from OB and could return to it, which actually does return to it and becomes one with OB the very instant we picture it there? This line is equal to $\dfrac{2l}{\sqrt{1-\dfrac{v^2}{c^2}}}$, when the original double light-line was $2l$.

Its lengthening therefore represents exactly the lengthening of time as given in the theory of relativity. We see from this that the theory proceeds as if we were taking the double journey of a light beam's departure and return between two fixed points as the standard of time. But we then perceive at once, intuitively, the relation of multiple times to the single, real time. Not only do the multiple times conjured up by the theory of relativity not disrupt the unity of a real time but they even imply and uphold it. The real observer inside his system is indeed aware of both the difference between, and the identity of, these two different times. He lives a psychological time, and, with this time, all the more or less expanded mathematical times merge; for in proportion as he spreads apart the hinged sticks of his toy—in the measure that he mentally accelerates the motion of his system—the light-lines lengthen, but they all fill the same lived duration. Without this unique, lived duration, without this real time common to all the mathematical times, what would it mean to say that they are contemporaneous, that they abide within the same interval? What meaning could we really find in such a statement?

Let us suppose (we shall return to this point shortly) that the observer in S is accustomed to measuring his time by a light-line, in other words, to pasting his psychological time to his light-line OB. Necessarily, psychological time and light-line (considered in the motionless system) will be synonymous for him. When, imagining his system in motion, he will think of his light-line as longer, he will say that time has lengthened; but he will also see that it is no longer psychological time. It is a time that is no longer, as before, both psychological and mathematical. It has become exclusively mathematical, incapable of being anyone's psychological time. As soon as a consciousness would wish to live one of these lengthened times O_1B_1, O_2B_2, etc., these latter would immediately retract into

OB, since the light-line would then no longer be perceived in imagination but in reality, and the system, until then only mentally set in motion, would claim actual immobility.

In short, therefore, the thesis of relativity here clearly intimates that an observer inside system *S,* picturing this system in motion at every possible speed, sees the mathematical time of his system lengthening with an increase in speed *if* this system's time had been identified with the light-lines OB, O_1B_1, O_2B_2, etc. All these different mathematical times are contemporaneous, in that all abide within the same psychological duration—that of the observer in *S.* They are only fictional times, moreover, since they cannot be lived differently from the first by anyone, neither by the *S* observer who perceives them all within the same duration, nor by any other real or possible observer. They hold on to the name "time" only because the first of the series, namely *OB,* measured the psychological duration of the observer in *S.* Then, by extension, we still apply the term "time" to the now lengthened light-lines of the supposedly moving system, forcing ourselves to forget that they all abide within the same duration. Let us, by all means, keep the name "time" for them: they are conventional times by definition, since they measure no real or possible duration.

But how explain, in a general way, this *rapprochement* between time and light-line? Why has the first of the light-lines, *OB,* been pasted by the observer in *S* to his psychological duration, imparting then the name and appearance of time to the successive lines O_1B_1, O_2B_2, etc., by a kind of contamination? We have already answered this question implicitly; it will nevertheless not be without profit to submit it to a new examination. But let us first see—while continuing to make a light-line of time—the second effect of the distortion of the figure.

2. LONGITUDINAL EFFECT OR "BREAKUP OF SIMULTANEITY"

As the light-lines that coincided in the original figure grow farther apart, the inequality becomes accentuated between two longitudinal light-lines, such as O_1A_1 and $A_1O'_1$, originally merged with the double light-line OA. Since, for us, the light-line is always time, we shall say that the moment A_1 is no longer in the middle of time interval $O_1A_1O'_1$, when the moment A was in the middle of the OAO interval. Now, whether the observer in system S assumes his system to be at rest or in motion, his assumption, a mere mental act, in no way influences his system's clocks. But it does influence their agreement, as we see. The clocks do not change; time changes. It is distorted and breaks up among them. It was equal times which, so to speak, went from O to A and returned from A to O in the original figure. Now the departure takes longer than the return. We easily see, moreover, that the second clock will lag behind the first by either $\dfrac{1}{\sqrt{1 - \dfrac{v^2}{c^2}}} \cdot \dfrac{lv}{c^2}$ or $\dfrac{lv}{c^2}$, depending upon whether we record it in seconds of the motionless system or the moving system. Since the clocks stay as they were, run as they have, preserve, consequently, the same relations with one another and remain synchronized as originally, they are found, in the mind of our observer, to lag more and more behind one another in proportion as his imagination accelerates the system's motion. Does he perceive himself motionless? There actually is simultaneity between the two instants when the clocks at O and A show the same time. Does he imagine himself in motion? These two instants, underscored by the two clocks showing the same time, cease by definition to be simultaneous, since the two light-lines have changed from equal to unequal. I mean that it was first equality, and now inequality, which *has just slipped* between the two clocks, they themselves not having budged. But have this equality and inequality the same degree of reality if they claim to apply to time? The first was *at one and the same time* an equality of light-lines and psychological durations, that is, of time in everyone's sense of the word. The second is nothing more than an inequality of light-lines, that is, of conventional times; it arises, however, among the same psychological durations as the first. And it is just because psychological duration continues to exist, unchanged, throughout all the successive imaginings of the observer, that he can consider all his imagined, conventional times as equivalent. He stands before figure *BOA;* he perceives a certain psychological duration that he measures by the double light-lines *OB* and *OA.* Now, without ceasing to look, therefore always perceiving this same duration, he sees, in his imagination, the double light-lines dissociate as they lengthen, the double longitudinal light-line splitting into two lines of unequal length, the inequality increasing with the speed. All these inequalities have come out of the original equality like the tubes out of a field glass; if it suits him, they will all instantly re-enter by telescoping. They are equivalent for him precisely because the true reality is the original equality, that is, the simultaneity of the moments indicated by the two clocks, and not the succession, purely imaginary and conventional, which the merely imagined motion of the system and the resultant breakup of its light-lines engender. All these breakups and successions are hence virtual; only the simultaneity is real. And it is because all these virtualities, all these varieties of dislocation abide inside the really perceived simultaneity that they are mathematically substitutable for it. All the same, there are, on the one hand, the imagined, the merely possible, while, on the other hand, are the perceived and the real.

Now, the fact that, consciously or not, the theory of relativity substitutes light-lines for time places one of its principles in full view. In a series of studies on the theory of relativity,[1] Edouard Guillaume has maintained that it essentially consists of making a clock out of the propagation of light, instead of the rotation of the earth. We believe there is much more than that in the theory of relativity. But we believe there is at least that. And we shall add that, in isolating this ingredient, one but emphasizes the theory's importance. In fact, still on this point, one thus establishes that the theory is the natural and perhaps necessary outcome of a long development. Let us

[1] *Revue de métaphysique* (May–June 1918, and October–December 1920). Cf. *La Théorie de la Relativité* (Lausanne, 1921).

briefly recall the penetrating and profound thoughts that Edouard le Roy set forth not long ago on the gradual perfecting of our means of measurement, especially the measurement of time.[2] He showed how a certain method of measuring enables us to establish laws and how these, once laid down, can react upon the method of measurement and compel it to be modified. With more particular reference to time, we have used the sidereal clock in the development of physics and astronomy; specifically, we have discovered the Newtonian law of attraction and the principle of the conservation of energy. But these results are incompatible with the constancy of the sidereal day, because, according to them, the tides must act as a brake upon the earth's rotation. Thus, the use of the sidereal clock leads to consequences which require the adoption of a new clock.[3] There is no doubt but that the progress of physics tends to present us with the optical clock—meaning the propagation of light—as the ultimate clock, the one that is the term of all those successive approximations. The theory of relativity records this outcome. And, as it is of the essence of physics to identify the thing with its measurement, the "light-line" becomes both the means of measuring time and time itself. But then, since the light-line elongates, while remaining itself, when we imagine as in motion yet leave at rest the system in which it is observed, we shall obtain multiple, equivalent times; and the hypothesis of the plurality of times, characteristic of the theory of relativity, will appear as conditioning the general evolution of physics as well. Times thus defined will indeed be physical times.[4] They will be only conceived times,

[2] *Bulletin de la Société française de philosophie*, February 1905.

[3] Cf. Emile Borel, *L'espace et le temps* (Paris: F. Alcan, 1922) p. 25.

[4] We have called them "mathematical," in the course of the present essay, in order to avoid any confusion. We are, indeed, continually comparing them with psychological time, distinguishing between the mathematical and the psychological and keeping this distinction ever in mind. Now, the difference between the psychological and the mathematical is clear; it is much less so between the psychological and the physical. The term "physical time" might at times have had a double meaning; "mathematical time" can have nothing ambiguous about it.

however, all except one, which will actually be perceived. The latter, always the same, is the time of common sense.

Let us sum up briefly. For a common-sense time, which can always be converted into psychological duration and which thus happens to be real by definition, the theory of relativity substitutes a time that can be converted into psychological duration only in the case of the system's immobility. In all other cases, this time, which was both light-line and duration, is no more than light-line—an elastic line that stretches as the speed attributed to the system increases. It cannot correspond to a new psychological duration, since it continues to fill this same duration. But small matter; the theory of relativity is a physical theory; it tends to ignore all psychological duration, as much in the first case as in all the others, and to retain of time nothing more than the light-line. As the latter either lengthens or contracts with the speed of the system, we thus obtain multiple, contemporaneous times. And that seems paradoxical because real duration continues to haunt us. But, on the other hand, it becomes very simple and quite natural when we substitute an extensible light-line for time and call simultaneity and succession instances of equality and inequality between light-lines whose interrelations evidently change with the system's state of rest or motion.

But these reflections upon light-lines would be incomplete if we limited ourselves to studying the transverse and longitudinal effects separately. We must now be present at their compounding. We shall see how the connection that must always obtain between longitudinal and transverse light-lines, whatever the system's speed, entails certain consequences regarding rigidity, and, therefore, extension as well. We shall thus obtain a lifelike picture of the interweaving of space and time in the theory of relativity. This interweaving appears clearly only after we have reduced time to a light-line. By means of the light-line, which is time but remains subtended by space, which lengthens as a result of the system's motion and thus gathers up, on the way, the space with which it makes time, we shall grasp, *in concreto*, in everyone's time and space, the very simple, initial fact expressed by the conception of a four-dimensional space-time in the theory of relativity.

3. TRANSVERSE-LONGITUDINAL EFFECT OR "LORENTZ CONTRACTION"

The special theory of relativity, we said, consists, in essence, of first picturing the double light-line BOA, then distorting it into such figures as $O_1B_1A_1O'_1$ through the system's motion, finally in making all these figures return, pull out, and return again one inside the other, while accustoming ourselves to thinking that they are *both* the first figure and the figures pulled out of it. In short, after mentally imparting every possible speed to the system, we entertain every possible vision of one and the same thing, this thing being deemed to coincide with all these visions at one and the same time. But the thing with which we are thus dealing is essentially a light-line. Let us consider the three points O, B, A of our first figure. Ordinarily, when we call them fixed points, we deal with them as if they were connected by rigid bars. In the theory of relativity, the bond becomes a ribbon of light which we would emit from O to B in such a way as to have it return upon itself and be caught again at O, another ribbon of light being emitted between O and A, touching A only to return to O. This means that time will now be amalgamated with space. Under the "rigid bar" assumption, the three points were connected in the instantaneous, or, if you prefer, in the eternal, in a word, outside of time; their relation in space was unchanging. But here, with elastic and distortable shafts of light which are representative of time, or, rather, are time itself, the relation of the three points falls under time's dependency.

To understand clearly the "contraction" that ensues, we have only to examine the successive light-figures, realizing that they are figures, tracks of light which we take in at a glance, and that we shall nevertheless have to treat the lines in them as if they were time. These light-lines alone being given, we must mentally reconstitute the space-lines, which will in general no longer be perceived in the figure itself. They can be no more than inferred, mentally reconstructed. The one exception, of course, is the light-figure of the system ruled motionless; thus, in our first figure, OB and OA are both flexible light-lines and rigid space-lines, the apparatus BOA being ruled at rest. But in our second light-figure, how are we to picture the apparatus with its two rigid space-lines supporting the two mirrors? Let us consider the position of the apparatus the moment B reaches B_1. If we drop perpendicular $B_1 O''_1$ on $O_1 A_1$, can we say that figure $B_1 O''_1 A_1$ is that of the apparatus? Clearly not, because if the equality of light-lines $O_1 B_1$ and $O'_1 B_1$ shows us that moments O''_1 and B_1 are truly contemporaneous, if $O''_1 B_1$ really retains its character of a rigid space-line, if, therefore, $O''_1 B_1$ really represents one of the arms of the apparatus, the inequality of light-lines $O_1 A_1$ and $O'_1 A_1$ shows us, on the other hand, that the two moments O''_1 and A_1 are successive. The length $O''_1 A_1$ therefore represents the other arm of the apparatus plus the distance covered by the apparatus during the interval of time that separates moment O''_1 from moment A_1. Hence, to obtain the length of this second arm, we must take the difference between $O''_1 A_1$ and the distance covered. This is easy to calculate. The length $O''_1 A_1$ is the arithmetical mean between $O_1 A_1$ and $O'_1 A_1$, and as the sum of these last two lengths is equal to $\dfrac{2l}{\sqrt{1 - \dfrac{v^2}{c^2}}}$, since the complete line $O_1 A_1 O'_1$ represents the same time as line $O_1 B_1 O'_1$, we see that the length of $O''_1 A_1$ is $\dfrac{l}{\sqrt{1 - \dfrac{v^2}{c^2}}}$. As for the space covered by the apparatus in the interval of time between moments O''_1 and A_1, we shall estimate it at once by observing that this interval is measured by the slowing of the clock located at the extremity of one of the apparatus arms over the clock located at the other, that is, by $\dfrac{1}{\sqrt{1 - \dfrac{v^2}{c^2}}} \cdot \dfrac{lv}{c^2}$. The distance covered is therefore $\dfrac{1}{\sqrt{1 - \dfrac{v^2}{c^2}}} \cdot \dfrac{lv^2}{c^2}$. And, consequently,

the length of the arm, which was l when at rest, becomes $\dfrac{l}{\sqrt{1 - \dfrac{v^2}{c^2}}} - \dfrac{lv^2}{c^2 \sqrt{1 - \dfrac{v^2}{c^2}}}$, that is, $l\sqrt{1 - \dfrac{v^2}{c^2}}$. We thus actually redis-

cover the "Lorentz contraction."

We see what this contraction means. The identification of time with the light-line causes the system's motion to have a double effect upon time: expansion of the second, breakup of simultaneity. In the difference $\dfrac{l}{\sqrt{1 - \dfrac{v^2}{c^2}}} - \dfrac{lv^2}{c^2 \sqrt{1 - \dfrac{v^2}{c^2}}}$ the first term

corresponds to the expansion effect, the second, to the breakup effect. In both cases, we can say that time alone (fictional time) is involved. But this combination of effects in time gives what we call a contraction of length in space.

We then grasp the very essence of the theory of relativity. It may be expressed in ordinary terms in this way: "Given a coinciding, at rest, of the rigid space-figure with the flexible light-figure, given, on the other hand, an ideal dissociation of these two figures as the result of a motion mentally attributed to the system, the successive distortions of the flexible light-figure at different speeds are all that count: the rigid space-figure will accommodate itself as best it can." As a matter of fact, we see that, during the system's motion, the longitudinal zigzag of light must keep the same length as the transverse zigzag, since the equality of these two times comes before all else. As, under these circumstances, the two rigid space-lines, the longitudinal and the transverse, cannot themselves remain equal, it is space that must give way. It will necessarily give way, the rigid diagram in lines of pure space being deemed only the registering of the global effect produced by the various changes in the flexible figure, that is, by the light-lines.

CHAPTER SIX

Four-Dimensional Space-Time

How the idea of a fourth dimension is ushered in; how immobility is expressed in terms of motion; how time amalgamates with space—the general conception of a four-dimensional space-time; what it adds to and subtracts from reality; twofold illusion to which it exposes us; the special character of this conception in the theory of relativity; particular error that we risk committing at this point; the real and the virtual; what the space-time amalgam actually represents

LET US now take leave of our light-figure with its successive distortions. We had to use it to give body to the abstractions of the theory of relativity and to bring out the postulates it implies. The relation previously established by us between multiple times and psychological time has perhaps become the clearer for it. And perhaps we have seen the door half opening through which the idea of a four-dimensional space-time will be introduced into the theory. It is to space-time that we shall now turn our attention.

The analysis just completed has already shown how this theory treats the relation of the thing to its expression. The thing is what is perceived; the expression is what the mind puts in place of the thing to make it amenable to calculation. The thing is given in a real vision; the expression corresponds at most to what we call a "phantasmal vision." Ordinarily, we conceive of phantasmal visions as ephemeral, surrounding the stable and firm nucleus of real vision. But the essence of the theory of relativity is to accord all these visions equal rank. The vision we call real would be only one of the phantasmal visions. This is all right in the sense that there is no way mathematically to express the difference between the two. But we must not conclude from that to a likeness in kind. Yet this is what we do when we confer a metaphysical meaning upon Minkowski's and Einstein's four-dimensional space-time continuum. Let us indeed see how this notion of space-time arises.

To that end, we have only to determine with precision the nature of the "phantasmal visions," in the case in which an observer inside a system S', having really perceived an invariable length l, would conceive the invariability of this length while mentally locating himself outside the system and then imagining it endowed with every possible speed. He would say to himself: "Since a line $A'B'$ in the moving system S', when passing before me in the motionless system in which I install myself, coincides with a length l of this system, it is because that line, at rest, is equal to $\dfrac{1}{\sqrt{1-\dfrac{v^2}{c^2}}} \cdot l$. Let us consider the square

$L^2 = \dfrac{1}{1-\dfrac{v^2}{c^2}} \cdot l^2$ of this magnitude. How much greater is it than

the square of l? By the quantity $\dfrac{1}{1-\dfrac{v^2}{c^2}} \cdot \dfrac{l^2 v^2}{c^2}$, which can be

written as $c^2 \left[\dfrac{1}{\sqrt{1-\dfrac{v^2}{c^2}}} \cdot \dfrac{lv}{c^2} \right]^2$. But, $\dfrac{1}{\sqrt{1-\dfrac{v^2}{c^2}}} \cdot \dfrac{lv}{c^2}$ is the exact

measure of the interval of time T which elapses for me, transported into system S, between two events respectively occurring at A' and B' which would appear simultaneous to me if I were in system S'. Hence, as the speed of S' increases from zero, the interval of time T broadens between the two events occurring at points A' and B', given in S' as simultaneous; but things so happen that the difference $L^2 - c^2T^2$ remains constant. It is this difference that I formerly called l^2." Thus, taking c as the unit of time, we can say that what is given to a real observer in S' as the fixity of a spatial magnitude, as the invariability of a square l^2, would appear to an imaginary observer in S as the constancy of the difference between the square of a space and the square of a time.

But we have just taken a special case. Let us generalize the question and first ask ourselves how the distance between two points in a physical system S' is expressed with respect to rectangular axes located in this system. We shall then try to find out how it will be expressed with respect to axes in system S with respect to which S' would become mobile.

If our space were two-dimensional, reduced to the size of the present page, if the two points considered were A' and B', whose respective distances from the axes $O'Y'$ and $O'X'$ are x'_1, y'_1 and x'_2, y'_2, it is clear that we would have

$$\overline{A'B'^2} = (x'_2 - x'_1)^2 + (y'_2 - y'_1)^2.$$

We could then consider any other system of axes motionless with respect to the first and thus give values for x'_1, x'_2, y'_1, y'_2 which would be generally different from the first: the sum of the two squares $(x'_2 - x'_1)^2$ and $(y'_2 - y'_1)^2$ would remain the same, since it would always be equal to $\overline{A'B'^2}$. Likewise, in a three-dimensional space, points A' and B' being then no longer assumed on plane $X'O'Y'$, being now defined by their distances x'_1, y'_1, z'_1, x'_2, y'_2, z'_2 from the three faces of a trihedral trirectangle whose vertex is O', we would ascertain the invariance of the sum $(x'_2 - x'_1)^2 + (y'_2 - y'_1)^2 + (z'_2 - z'_1)^2$. It is by this very invariance that the fixity of the distance between A' and B' would be expressed for an observer located in S'.

But let us suppose that our observer mentally enters system S with respect to which S' is ruled in motion. Let us also suppose that he refers points A' and B' to axes located in his new system, placing himself, moreover, in the simplified circumstances we described further back when we were working out the Lorentz equations. The respective distances from points A' and B' to the three rectangular planes intersecting at S will now be x_1, y_1, z_1; x_2, y_2, z_2. The square of the distance $A'B'$ between our two points will, moreover, still be given as a sum of three squares $(x_2 - x_1)^2 + (y_2 - y_1)^2 + (z_2 - z_1)^2$. But, according to the Lorentz equations, even if the last two squares of this sum are identical with the last two of the preceding sum, this does not hold for the first, because these equations give us for x_2 and x_1, respectively, the values $\dfrac{1}{\sqrt{1-\dfrac{v^2}{c^2}}}(x'_1 + vt')$ and $\dfrac{1}{\sqrt{1-\dfrac{v^2}{c^2}}}(x'_2 + vt')$; so that the first square will be $\dfrac{1}{1-\dfrac{v^2}{c^2}}(x'_2 - x'_1)^2$.

We naturally find ourselves confronting the particular case which we were examining just before. We had, in fact, been considering a certain length $A'B'$ in system S', that is, the distance separating two instantaneous and simultaneous events occurring at A' and B', respectively. But we now wish to generalize the question. Let us therefore suppose that the two events are successive for the observer in S'. If one occurs at moment t'_1, and the other, at moment t'_2, the Lorentz equations will give us

$$x_1 = \frac{1}{\sqrt{1-\dfrac{v^2}{c^2}}}(x'_1 + vt'_1)$$

$$x_2 = \frac{1}{\sqrt{1-\dfrac{v^2}{c^2}}}(x'_2 + vt'_2)$$

so that our first square will become

$$\frac{1}{1-\dfrac{v^2}{c^2}}\left[(x'_2 - x'_1) + v(t'_2 - t'_1)\right]^2$$

and our original sum of three squares will be replaced by

$$\frac{1}{1-\dfrac{v^2}{c^2}}\left[(x'_2 - x'_1) + v(t'_2 - t'_1)\right]^2 + (y_2 - y_1)^2 + (z_2 - z_1)^2$$

a magnitude that depends upon v and is no longer invariant. But if, in this expression, we look at the first term $\dfrac{1}{1-\dfrac{v^2}{c^2}}\left[(x'_2 - x'_1) + v(t'_2 - t'_1)\right]^2$, which gives us the value of

$(x_2 - x_1)^2$, we see [1] that it exceeds $(x'_2 - x'_1)^2$ by the quantity

$$\frac{1}{1 - \dfrac{v^2}{c^2}} \cdot c^2 \left[(t'_2 - t'_1) + \frac{v(x'_2 - x'_1)}{c^2} \right]^2 - c^2(t'_2 - t'_1)^2.$$

Now, the Lorentz equations give:

$$\frac{1}{1 - \dfrac{v^2}{c^2}} \left[(t'_2 - t'_1) + \frac{v(x'_2 - x'_1)}{c^2} \right]^2 = (t_2 - t_1)^2.$$

We therefore have

$$(x_2 - x_1)^2 - (x'_2 - x'_1)^2 = c^2(t_2 - t_1)^2 - c^2(t'_2 - t'_1)^2$$

or

$$(x_2 - x_1)^2 - c^2(t_2 - t_1)^2 = (x'_2 - x'_1)^2 - c^2(t'_2 - t'_1)^2$$

or finally

$$(x_2 - x_1)^2 + (y_2 - y_1)^2 + (z_2 - z_1)^2 - c^2(t_2 - t_1)^2$$
$$= (x'_2 - x'_1)^2 + (y'_2 - y'_1)^2 + (z'_2 - z'_1)^2 - c^2(t'_2 - t'_1)^2$$

a result which could be worded as follows: If the observer in S' had considered, instead of the sum of three squares

$$(x'_2 - x'_1)^2 + (y'_2 - y'_1)^2 + (z'_2 - z'_1)^2$$

the expression

$$(x'_2 - x'_1)^2 + (y'_2 - y'_1)^2 + (z'_2 - z'_1)^2 - c^2(t'_2 - t'_1)_2$$

in which a fourth square enters, he would have re-established, through the introduction of time, the invariance that had ceased to exist in space.

Our calculations may have appeared a bit clumsy. And so they actually are. Nothing would have been simpler than to state at once that the expression

$$(x_2 - x_1)^2 + (y_2 - y_1)^2 + (z_2 - z_1)^2 - c^2(t_2 - t_1)^2$$

does not change when we subject its component terms to the Lorentz transformation. But that would have been to accord equal rank to every system in which every measurement is deemed to have been made. The mathematician and the physicist must do so, since they are not seeking to interpret the space-time of the theory of relativity in terms of reality but simply to make use of it. On the other hand, our own aim is

[1] One can verify this easily enough.

this very interpretation. We therefore had to set out from measurements taken in system S' by the observer in S'—the only real measurements attributable to a real observer—and to consider the measurements made in other systems as alterations or distortions of the former, alterations and distortions so coordinated that certain connections among the measurements remain the same. The detour we just made was therefore necessary to preserve the S' observer's central position and thus set the stage for the analysis of space-time, which we shall present shortly. It was also necessary, as we shall see, to establish a distinction between the case in which the observer in S' perceived events A' and B' as simultaneous, and the case in which he notes them down as successive. This distinction would have vanished if we had made simultaneity only the special case in which $t'_2 - t'_1 = 0$; we would thus have reabsorbed it into succession; every difference in kind would again have been suppressed between the measurements really made by the observer in S' and the merely imagined measurements that observers outside the system would make. But small matter for the moment. We are merely showing how the theory of relativity is actually guided by considerations that precede the positing of a four-dimensional space-time.

We said that the expression of the square of the distance between two points A' and B', referred to two axes at right angles in a two-dimensional space, is $(x_2 - x_1)^2 + (y_2 - y_1)^2$, if x_1, y_1, x_2, y_2 are their respective distances from the two axes. We added that in a three-dimensional space this expression would become $(x_2 - x_1)^2 + (y_2 - y_1)^2 + (z_2 - z_1)^2$. Nothing prevents us from imagining spaces of 4, 5, 6 . . . n dimensions. The square of the distance between two points would be given in them by a sum of 4, 5, 6 . . . n squares, each of these squares being that of the difference between the distances from points A' and B' to one of the 4, 5, 6 . . . n planes. Let us then consider our expression $(x_2 - x_1)^2 + (y_2 - y_1)^2 + (z_2 - z_1)^2 - c^2(t_2 - t_1)^2$. If the sum of the first three terms were constant, it could express the constancy of the distance, as we conceived it in our three-dimensional space before the theory of relativity. But in essence the latter consists in saying that we must introduce the fourth term to get this constancy. Why would this fourth term not correspond to a fourth dimension? Two considerations seem at once to be opposed to this, if we hold to our expression for distance: on the one hand, the square $(t_2 - t_1)^2$ is preceded by a *minus* instead of a *plus* sign; and, on the other, it is affected by a coefficient c^2 different from unity. But as, on a fourth axis that would be representative of time, times would necessarily have to be conveyed as lengths, we can rule that, on this axis, a second will have the length c: our coefficient will thus become unity. Moreover, if we consider a time τ such that we have $t = \tau\sqrt{-1}$ and if, in a general way, we replace t by the imaginary quantity $\tau\sqrt{-1}$, our fourth square will be $-\tau^2$, and we shall then really be dealing with a sum of four squares. Let us agree to designate by Δx, Δy, Δz, $\Delta\tau$ the four differences $x_2 - x_1$, $y_2 - y_1$, $z_2 - z_1$, $\tau_2 - \tau_1$, which are the respective increments of x, y, z, τ when we pass from x_1 to x_2, from y_1 to y_2, from z_1 to z_2, from τ_1 to τ_2; and let us designate by Δs the interval between the two points A' and B'. We shall have:

$$\Delta s^2 = \Delta x^2 + \Delta y^2 + \Delta z^2 + \Delta\tau^2.$$

And from then on nothing will prevent us from believing that s is a distance, or, rather, an interval, in both space and time: the fourth square would correspond to the fourth dimension of a space-time continuum in which time and space would be amalgamated.

Nor is there anything to keep us from imagining the two points A' and B' as so infinitely adjacent that $A'B'$ may as well be a curve element. A finite increase like Δx will then become an infinitesimal increase dx and we shall have the differential equation

$$ds^2 = dx^2 + dy^2 + dz^2 + d\tau^2$$

from which we can rise again through a summation of infinitely small elements, through "integration," to the interval s between two points of, this time, any line at all, occupying both space and time, which we shall call AB. We shall write it as

$$s = \int_A^B \sqrt{dx^2 + dy^2 + dz^2 + d\tau^2},$$

an expression of which we must be cognizant, but to which we shall not return in what follows. We shall gain more by making direct use of the considerations that have led us to it.[2]

We have just seen how the notation of a fourth dimension is introduced automatically, so to speak, into the theory of relativity. This undoubtedly accounts for the oft-expressed opinion that we are indebted to this theory for the earliest suggestion of a four-dimensional environment merging time and space. What has not been sufficiently noted is that a fourth dimension of space is suggested by every spatialization of time; it has therefore always been implicit in our science and language. Actually, we could sift it out of the usual conception of time in a more precise, at least more imagistic, form than out of the theory of relativity. But, in the usual conception, the comparison of time to a fourth dimension is understood, whereas the physics of relativity is obliged to introduce it into its calculations. And this leads to the double effect of endosmosis and exosmosis between time and space, to their reciprocal encroachment, which the Lorentz equations appear to express: it now becomes necessary, in locating a point, to indicate explicitly its position in time as well as in space. Nonetheless, Minkowski's and Einstein's space-time remains a *species* of which the ordinary spatialization of time in a four-dimensional space is the *genus*. The course we have to follow is then completely laid out. We must begin by seeking the general meaning of the introduction of a four-dimensional environment that would unite time and space. Then we shall ask ourselves what we add to, or subtract from, this meaning when we conceive the relation between spatial and temporal dimensions in the manner of Minkowski and Einstein. Even now, one begins to see that, if the popular conception of a space joined to spatialized time quite naturally takes mental shape as a

---

[2] The reader who is something of a mathematician will have noticed that the expression $ds^2 = dx^2 + dy^2 + dz^2 - c^2dt^2$ can be considered, as it stands, as corresponding to a hyperbolic space-time. Minkowski's artifice, described above, consists in giving Euclidean form to this space-time by the substitution of the imaginary variable $ct\sqrt{-1}$ for the variable t.

four-dimensional environment, and if this environment is fictional because it merely symbolizes the convention of spatializing time, the same is true for the species of which this four-dimensional environment is the genus. In any case, species and genus will perforce have the same degree of reality and the space-time of the theory of relativity will hardly be any more incompatible with our long-standing concept of duration than was a four-dimensional space-and-time symbolizing both ordinary space and spatialized time. Still, we cannot dispense with a more detailed examination of Minkowski's and Einstein's space-time, when once we have turned our attention to a general four-dimensional space-and-time. Let us first apply ourselves to the latter.

We have difficulty in imagining a new dimension if we set out from a three-dimensional space, since experience does not reveal a fourth. But nothing is simpler if it is a two-dimensional space that we endow with this added dimension. We can conjure up flat beings, living on a surface, merging with it, aware of only two dimensions of space. One of them will have been led by his calculations to postulate the existence of a third dimension. His fellow beings, shallow in the double sense of the word, will no doubt refuse to heed him; he himself will not succeed in imagining what his understanding will have been able to conceive. But we, who live in a three-dimensional space, would have the actual perception of what he would merely have represented as possible: we would be able to give an exact account of what he would have added by introducing a new dimension. And, as we ourselves would be doing something of the kind if we imagined, limited as we are to three dimensions, that we were immersed in a four-dimensional environment, it would be almost in this way that we would picture this fourth dimension that first seemed unimaginable. True, this would not be quite the same thing. For a space of more than three dimensions is a mere idea in the mind and cannot correspond to any reality. Whereas three-dimensional space is that of our experience. Therefore, when, in what follows, we use our actually perceived three-dimensional space to give a body to the formulations of a mathematician subject to a flat universe—formulations conceivable for him but not imaginable—that does not mean that a four-dimensional space can or does exist that is capable, in its turn, of bringing our own mathematical conceptions into being in concrete form when they transcend our three-dimensional world. This would be unduly favoring those who immediately interpret the theory of relativity metaphysically. The only aim of the artifice we are about to employ is to supply the theory with an imaginative prop, so to render it clearer and thus make it easier to perceive the errors into which hasty inferences would lead us.

We are therefore simply going to return to the hypothesis from which we had set out when we drew two axes at right angles and examined a line $A'B'$ on the same plane as they. We gave ourselves only the surface of a sheet of paper. This two-dimensional world is endowed by the theory of relativity with an additional dimension, which is time: the constant is no longer $dx^2 + dy^2$ but $dx^2 + dy^2 - c^2dt^2$. To be sure, this additional dimension is of an altogether special nature, since the constant would be $dx^2 + dy^2 + dt^2$, without needing an artifice to lead it around to this form, if time were a dimension like the others. We shall have to keep in mind this characteristc difference, with which we have already been occupied and upon which we shall soon focus our attention. But we are bypassing it for the moment, since the theory of relativity itself invites us to do so: if it has had recourse here to an artifice, and posited an imaginary time, it was precisely in order that its constant might retain the form of a sum of four squares, each with unity as coefficient, and in order that the new dimension might be provisionally assimilable to the others. Let us therefore ask, in a general way, what we bring to, and, what, perhaps, we also take away from, a two-dimensional universe when we turn its time into an extra dimension. We shall then take account of the special role which this new dimension plays in the theory of relativity.

We cannot repeat often enough: the mathematician's time

is necessarily a time that is measured, and therefore, a spatialized time. We need not take the position of relativity: from any standpoint, mathematical time can be treated as an additional dimension of space (we pointed this out more than thirty years ago). Let us imagine a surface universe reduced to plane P and, on this plane, let us consider a mobile M that describes any line whatever, for example, a circumference, starting at a certain point of origin. We who live in a three-dimensional world, will be able to picture this mobile M leading a line MN perpendicular to the plane, a line whose changing length would at each instant be recording the time elapsed from the point of origin. The extremity N of this line will describe in the three-dimensional space a curve which, in the case at hand, will be spiral in form. It is easy to see that this curve laid out in the three-dimensional space yields all the temporal details of change in the two-dimensional space P. The distance from any point on the spiral to plane P indicates, in effect, the moment of time with which we are dealing, and the tangent to the curve at this point gives us, by its inclination to plane P, the speed of the moving point at this moment.[3] Thus, it will be thought, the "two-dimensional curve" [4] delineates only a part of the reality found on plane P because it is only *space,* in the P inhabitants' sense of the word. On the other hand, the "three-dimensional curve" contains this reality in its entirety: it has three dimensions of space for us; it would be three-dimensional space-and-time for a two-dimensional mathematician living on plane P who, incapable of visualizing the third dimension, would be led to conceive it through his ascertainment of motion, and to express it analytically. He could then learn from us that a three-dimensional curve actually exists as an image.

Moreover, once the three-dimensional curve, at once both

[3] A very simple calculation would demonstrate this.

[4] We are obliged to use these hardly correct expressions, "two-dimensional curve" and "three-dimensional curve," to refer to the plane and spiral curves. There is no other way to indicate the spatial and temporal implications of one and the other.

space and time, has been posited, the two-dimensional curve would appear to the mathematician on the flat universe like a mere projection onto the plane he inhabits. It would be only the surface and spatial aspect of a solid reality which would have to be called both time and space.

In brief, the form of a three-dimensional curve here gives us information about both the plane trajectory and the temporal details of a motion in two-dimensional space. More generally, *what is given as motion in a space of any number of dimensions can be represented as form in a space of one more dimension.*

But is this representation really adequate to what is represented? Does it contain quite what the latter contains? At first glance we might think so, from what we have just said. But the truth is that it includes more in one respect, less in another, and that if the two things appear interchangeable, it is because our mind surreptitiously subtracts what is superfluous in the representation, and no less surreptitiously inserts what is lacking.

To begin with the second point, it is obvious that *becoming,* properly so called, has been eliminated. This is because science has to do with it only in the case at hand. What is its aim? Simply to know where the mobile will be at any moment in its course. It therefore always betakes itself to the extremity of an interval already traversed; it is interested only in the result, once that is obtained; if it can portray at one stroke every result at every moment, and in such a way as to know what result corresponds to what moment, it has achieved the same success as the child who has become able to read an entire word all at once instead of spelling it letter by letter. This is what happens in the case of the point-to-point correspondence between our circle and spiral. But this correspondence has meaning only because we mentally *traverse* the curve and occupy points on it *successively.* If we have been able to replace this succession by a juxtaposition, real time by a spatialized time, *becoming* by the *become,* it is because we retain becoming, real duration, within us; when the child actually reads a word all at once, he is spelling it virtually letter by letter. Let us not therefore imagine that our three-dimensional curve gives us, as if crystallized together, the motion by which the curve is outlined on the plane and this plane curve itself. It has merely extracted from becoming what is of interest to science, and science can use this extract only because our mind will re-establish the eliminated becoming or will feel able to do so. In this sense, the curve of $n + 1$ dimensions, *already outlined,* which would be the equivalent of the curve of n dimensions *being outlined* really represents less than it claims to represent.

But, in another sense, it represents more. Subtracting here, adding there, it is doubly inadequate.

We have obtained it, as a matter of fact, by means of a clearly defined operation, through the circular motion, on plane P, of a point M that led the line MN of a length varying with the time elapsed. This plane, circle, line, motion, these are the completely determinate elements of the operation through which the figure was outlined. But the figure all outlined does not necessarily imply this mode of generation. Even if it does imply it, the figure may have been the outcome of the motion of a different line, perpendicular to a different plane, whose extremity M has described, at quite different speeds, a curve that was not a circumference. Let us, in fact, consider any plane and project our spiral upon it; the latter will be as clearly representative of the new plane curve, traversed at new speeds and amalgamated to new times. If, therefore, in the sense just described, the spiral contains less than the circumference and the motion we claim to rediscover in it, in another sense, it contains more; once accepted as the amalgam of a certain plane figure with a certain mode of motion, we can discover an infinity of other plane figures in it as well, respectively completed by an infinity of other motions. In short, as we announced, this representation is doubly inadequate: it both falls short and goes too far. And we can guess the reason for this. By adding a dimension to the space in which we happen to exist, we can undoubtedly picture a *process* or a *becoming,* noted in the old space, as a *thing* in this new space. But as we have substituted the *completely made* for what we perceive *being made,* we have, on the one hand, eliminated the becoming inherent in time and, on the other hand, introduced the possibility of an infinity of other processes through which the thing could just as well have been constructed. Along the time in which we found the progressive genesis of this thing, there was a clearly defined mode of generation; but, in the new space, increased by one dimension, in which the thing is spread out at one stroke by the joining of time to the original space, we are free to imagine an infinity of equally possible modes of generation; and the one that we have actually found, though it alone is real, no longer appears as privileged: we shall line it up—wrongly—alongside the others.

Already we catch a glimpse of the twofold danger to which we expose ourselves when we symbolize time by a fourth dimension of space. On the one hand, we risk taking the unfolding of the whole past, present, and future history of the universe for a mere running of our consciousness along this history given all at one stroke in eternity; events would no longer file before us, it is we who would pass before their alignment. And, on the other hand, in the space-and-time or space-time that we shall have thus constituted, we shall believe that we are free to choose among an infinity of possible repartitions of space and time. Yet it was out of a well-determined space and time that this space-time had been built: only a certain special distribution in space and time was real. But we make no distinction between it and all other possible distributions; or rather, we see no more than an infinity of possible distributions, the real distribution being no more than one of them. In short, we forget that, measurable time being of necessity symbolized by space, there is both more and less in this space dimension considered as symbol than in time itself.

But we shall perceive these two points more clearly in the following manner. We have been imagining a two-dimensional universe. This will be the indefinitely extended plane *P*. Each of the successive states of this universe will be an instantaneous image, taking up the whole plane and comprising the totality of objects, all flat, of which this universe is made. The plane will therefore be like a screen upon which the cinematography of the universe would be run off, with the difference however that here there is no cinematography external to the screen, no photography projected from without; the image takes form on the screen spontaneously. Now, the inhabitants of plane *P* will be able to imagine the succession of cinematographic images in their space in two different ways. They will split into two camps, depending upon whether they adhere more to the data of experience or to the symbolism of science.

The first will be of the opinion that there really are successive images, but not all lined up on a roll of film; and this, for two reasons: (1) Where would the film be housed? By hypothesis, each of the images, covering the screen by itself, fills up all of a perhaps infinite space, that of the universe. These images therefore really have no alternative but to exist only successively; they cannot be given globally. Besides, time really presents itself to our consciousness as duration and succession, attributes irreducible to any other and distinct from juxtaposition. (2) On a film, everything would be predetermined, or, if you prefer, determined. Illusory, therefore, would be our consciousness of choosing, acting, creating. If there is succession and duration, it is only because reality hesitates, feels its way, gradually works out the unforeseeable novelty. To be sure, the share of absolute determination in the universe is great; this is exactly why a mathematical physics is possible. But what is predetermined is virtually *already made* and endures only through its connection with what is *in the making*, with what is real duration and succession; we must take this interweaving into account and then see that the past, present, and future history of the universe cannot be given globally on a roll of film.[5]

The others would reply: "In the first place, we have nothing

<hr>

[5] With reference to this point, to what we called "the *cinematographic* mechanism of thought," and with reference to our cinematographic representation of things, see *L'Evolution créatrice* (*Creative Evolution*), Chap. IV.

to do with your so-called unforeseeableness. The aim of science is to calculate and therefore to foresee; we shall therefore disregard your feeling of indeterminacy, which is perhaps only an illusion. Now, you say that there is no room in the universe to house images other than the image designated as present. This would be true if the universe were doomed to having only two dimensions. But we can imagine a third to which our senses cannot attain and across which our consciousness would travel when unfolding in "time." Thanks to this third dimension of space, all the images making up all the past and future moments of the universe are given at one stroke along with the present image, not laid out with respect to one another like frames on a roll of film (for that, indeed, there would be no room), but arranged in a different order, which we do not succeed in imagining, but which we can nevertheless conceive. To live in time consists in traversing this third dimension, that is, in itemizing it, in perceiving one by one the images that it enables to be juxtaposed. The apparent indeterminateness of what we are about to perceive lies merely in the fact that it has not yet been perceived; it is an objectivizing of our ignorance.[6] We believe that images are created in so far as they appear, precisely because they seem *to appear* to us, that is, to arise before us and for us, to come toward us. But let us not forget that all motion is reciprocal or relative: if we perceive them coming toward us, it is also true to say that we are going toward them. They are there in reality; lined up, they await us; we march past them. Let us not say, therefore, that events or accidents befall us; it is we who befall them. And we would immediately ascertain this if we were as acquainted with the third dimension as with the others."

I shall now imagine that I have been appointed arbitrator between the two camps. Turning to those who have just spoken, I would say to them: "Let me first congratulate you upon having only two dimensions, for you are thus going to

---

[6] In the pages devoted to the "cinematographic mechanism of thought," we once showed that this way of reasoning is natural to the human mind (*ibid.*).

obtain for your thesis a proof for which I would vainly seek, were I to pursue an argument analogous to yours in the space into which fate has thrust me. I happen, as a matter of fact, to live in a three-dimensional space; and when I agree with some philosophers that it can really have a fourth, I am saying something that is perhaps absurd in itself, although mathematically conceivable. A superman, whom I would appoint, in my turn, as arbitrator between them and me would perhaps explain that the idea of a fourth dimension is obtained through the extension of certain mathematical habits contracted in our space (entirely as you obtained the idea of a third dimension), but that this time the idea does not and cannot correspond to any reality. There is, nevertheless, a three-dimensional space, where I happen to be: this is a good thing for you, and I shall be able to give you information. Yes, you have guessed right in believing that the coexistence of images like yours, each extending over an infinite 'surface,' is possible when it is impossible in the truncated space where your whole universe appears to you to abide at each instant. It is enough that these images—which we call 'flat'—pile up, as we say, one on top of the other. There they are, all piled up. I see your 'solid,' as we call it, universe; it is made of the piling up of all your flat images, past, present, and future. I also see your consciousness traveling perpendicularly to these superimposed 'planes,' never taking cognizance of any but the one it crosses, perceiving it as the present, then remembering the one it leaves behind, but ignorant of those which are in front and which enter its present, one at a time, forthwith enriching its past.

"But, this is what strikes me further.

"I have taken random images, or rather pellicles without images on them, to represent your future, which I do not know. I have thus piled up on top of the present state of your universe future states that remain blank for me; they form a pendant to the past states on the other side of the present state, which past states I perceive as definite images. But I am by no means sure that your future coexists in this way with your present. It is you who are telling me it does. I have drawn my figure to your specifications, but your hypothesis remains an hypothesis. Do not forget that it is an hypothesis and that it merely expresses certain properties of a very special class of events, carved out of the immensity of the real, with which physical science is occupied. Now, I can tell you, letting you benefit from my experience of the third dimension, that your representation of time by space is going to give you both more and less than you wish to represent.

"It will give you less, because the heap of piled-up images comprising every state of the universe contains nothing that either implies or explains the motion by which your space P invests them one at a time, or by which (it amounts to the same thing, according to you), one at a time, they come to fill the space P where you are. I am well aware that, in your eyes, this motion is of no consequence. Since all the images are given virtually—and this is your conviction—since we are theoretically in a position to take the one we want out of the front part of the pile (in this lies the calculation or prevision of an event), the motion that would oblige you first to pass along images lying between that one and the present image— the motion that would actually be time—seems to you a mere 'delay' or hindrance brought to bear, in actuality, upon a perception that, by right, is immediate; there would be here only a deficiency in your empirical knowledge, exactly made up for by your mathematical science. In a word, it would be something negative; and we would not be claiming more, but less than we had, when we posit a succession, that is, a necessity for leafing through the album, when all the leaves are there. But I, who experience this three-dimensional universe and can there actually perceive the motion imagined by you, I must inform you that you are looking at only one aspect of mobility and, consequently, of duration; the other, essential, one escapes you. We can, no doubt, consider every part of every future, predetermined state of the universe as theoretically piled up one on top of the other, and logically given in advance; we only express their predetermination in this way.

But these parts, constitutive of what we call the physical world, are framed in others upon which your calculation has until now had no hold and which you declare calculable as the result of an entirely hypothetical assimilation; these are the organic, the conscious. I, who have been inserted into the organic world through my body, and into the world of consciousness through my mind, I perceive its forward progress as a gradual enrichment, a continuity of invention and creation. For me, time is what is most real and necessary; it is the fundamental condition of action—what am I saying?—it is action itself; and my obligation to live it, the impossibility of ever encroaching upon the coming interval of time, would be enough to show me—if I did not have it as an immediate experience—that the future is really open, unforeseen, indeterminate. Do not consider me a metaphysician, if you thus refer to the man of dialectical constructions. I have constructed nothing. I have merely noted. I am confiding to you what greets my senses and consciousness: what is immediately given must be considered real as long as we have not convicted it of being a mere appearance; if you see it as illusory, it is up to you to prove this. But you suspect it as illusory only because you yourself are creating a metaphysical construction. Or, rather, the construction has already been created; it dates from Plato, who held time to be a mere deprivation of eternity; and most ancient and modern metaphysicians have adopted it just as it stands, because it does, in fact, answer a fundamental need of human understanding. Made to establish laws, that is, to extract certain unchanging relations from the changing flux of things, our understanding is naturally inclined to see only them; they alone exist for it; it therefore fulfills its function, answers its purpose, in taking up a position outside of the time that flows and endures. But the mind, which extends beyond sheer understanding, is well aware that, if the essential work of intelligence is the extraction of laws, it is in order that our action may know what to take into account, so that our will may have a better grip on things: the understanding treats duration as a deficiency, a pure negation, in order that we may be able to work with the greatest possible efficiency within this duration, which is, however, what is most positive in the world. The metaphysics of most metaphysicians is therefore only the very law of the functioning of the understanding, which is one of the faculties of mind, but not mind itself. The latter, in its integrality, takes account of integral experience; and the integrality of our experience is duration. Hence, no matter what you do, you eliminate something, even what is essential, in replacing the singly passing states of the universe by a block universe posited once and for all.[7]

"You are thereby claiming *less* than you should. But, in another sense, you are claiming *more*.

"You are, in fact, convinced that your plane P passes through every image, ready and waiting for you, of all the successive moments of the universe. Or—what amounts to the same thing—you are convinced that each of these images given in the instantaneous or in eternity has been doomed, by reason of a weakness in your perception, to seem to you to be passing onto your plane P one at a time. It makes little difference, moreover, whether you express yourself in one way or the other; in both cases there is a plane P—this is space—and a shift of this plane in a direction parallel to itself—this is time— which makes the plane traverse the totality of the once-and-for-all posited block. But if the block is really given, you can just as easily intersect it by any other plane P' again moving parallel to itself and thus traversing the totality of the real in a different direction.[8] You will have effected a new distribution

---

[7] In *L'Evolution créatrice* (*Creative Evolution*), Chap. IV, we dwelled at length upon the connection established by metaphysicians between the *block* and the images given one at a time.

[8] It is true that, in our usual conception of spatialized time, we have never tried to shift the direction of time *in actual fact*, and to imagine a new distribution of the four-dimensional space-time continuum: it would offer no advantage and give incoherent results, whereas this operation seems to force itself upon us in the theory of relativity. Still, as we see it, the amalgam of time with space, which we claim to be characteristic of this theory, is, strictly speaking, conceivable in the everyday theory, even though it may look different there.

of space and time just as legitimate as the first, since only the solid block has absolute reality. In fact, such is actually your hypothesis. You imagine that, by adding an extra dimension, you have obtained a three-dimensional space-time that can be divided into space and time in an infinite number of ways; yours, the one you experience, would be only one of them; it would rank with the others. But I, who *see* what all these experiences of observers attached to and moving with your P' planes would be, experiences which you merely imagine, I can inform you that, having the vision of an image composed of points borrowed from all the real moments in the universe, they would live in incoherence and absurdity. The aggregate of these incoherent and absurd images does, indeed, reproduce the block, but it is only because the block has been constituted in quite another manner—by a particular plane moving in a particular direction—that a block exists at all, and that we can play about with the fantasy of mentally reconstituting it by means of any plane at all moving in some other direction. To rank these fantasies with reality, to say that the motion which is actually productive of the block is only one of a number of possible motions, is to disregard the second point to which I just drew your attention: in the block which is *ready-made* and set free of the duration where it was *being made,* the result, once obtained and cut off, no longer bears the clear stamp of the work by which we obtained it. A thousand different mental operations, would just as easily recompose it in idea, even though it has really been composed in a certain unique way. After the house has been built, our imagination can roam all over it and rebuild it just as easily by first setting the roof, and then hitching the stories to it, one at a time. Who would place this method on the same footing with that of the architect and consider both equivalent? Looking closely, we see that the architect's method is the only effective way to compose the whole, that is, to make it; the others, despite appearances, are only ways to decompose it, that is, in short, to unmake it; there exist, then, as many of these ways as we like. What could be built only in a certain order can be demolished any which way."

Such are the two points we must never lose sight of when we join time to space by endowing the latter with an extra dimension. We have taken the most general case; we have not yet considered the very special look of this new dimension in the theory of relativity. This is because every time the theoreticians of relativity leave pure science to give us an idea of the metaphysical reality which that mathematics expresses, they begin by implicitly allowing the fourth dimension *at least* the attributes of the other three, even bringing in something more. In talking about their space-time, they take the following two points for granted: (1) Every partitioning of it in space and time must be accorded equal rank (it is true that in the hypothesis of relativity, these partitionings can only be made according to a special law, to which we shall soon recur); (2) our experience of successive events only illumines, one by one, the points of a line given all at once. They seem not to have realized that the mathematical expression of time, necessarily imparting to it, in effect, the characteristics of space and requiring that the fourth dimension, whatever its own qualities, first have those of the other three, will sin both by excess and deficiency, as we have just shown. Whoever does not provide a corrective here runs the risk of mistaking the philosophical meaning of the theory of relativity and of giving a mathematical representation the status of a transcendent reality. We shall be persuaded of this by repairing to certain passages in Eddington's already classic volume: "Events do not happen; they are there and we meet them on our way. The 'formality of taking place' is merely an indication that the observer, in his voyage of exploration, has passed into the absolute future of the event in question, and is of no great significance." [9] Before that, we read in one of the first works on the theory of relativity, by Silberstein,[10] that Wells had

[9] Arthur S. Eddington, *Space, Time and Gravitation* (Cambridge: Cambridge University Press, 1920), p. 151.

[10] Ludwik Silberstein, *The Theory of Relativity* (London: Macmillan and Co., Ltd., 1914), p. 134.

wondrously anticipated this theory when he had his "time-traveler" say that "there is no difference between time and space except that our consciousness moves along time."

But we must now turn our attention to the special look which the fourth dimension takes on in the space-time of Minkowski and Einstein. Here, the constant ds^2 is no longer a sum of four squares, each having the coefficient of unity, as it would be if time were a dimension like the others: the fourth square, assigned the coefficient c^2, must be subtracted from the sum of the preceding three, and thus proves a case apart. We can smooth out this singularity of mathematical expression by a suitable artifice; it nonetheless remains in the thing expressed and the mathematician advises us of this by saying that the first three dimensions are "real" and the fourth, "imaginary." Let us examine this special form of space-time as closely as possible.

But let us at once announce the result toward which we are heading. It will necessarily resemble greatly the one that our inquiry into multiple times gave us; it can, indeed, be only a new expression of it. Against common sense and the philosophic tradition, which declare for a single time, the theory of relativity had first appeared to assert the plurality of times. On closer inspection, we had never found more than a single real time, that of the physicist engaged in building up his science; the others are virtual, that is, imaginary times, attributed by him to virtual, that is, phantasmal observers. Each of these phantasmal observers, suddenly coming to life, would install himself in the real duration of the former real observer, who would become phantasmal in his turn. Thus, the usual idea of real time quite naturally continues to hold good with, in addition, a mental construction intended to represent how, if one applies the Lorentz equations, the mathematical expression of electromagnetic facts remains the same for the observer considered motionless and for the observer to whom any uniform motion at all is attributed. Now, Minkowski's and Einstein's space-time represents nothing else. If by four-dimensional space-time we understand a real environment in which real beings and objects evolve, the space-time of the theory of relativity is everyone's, for we all make the vague gesture of positing a four-dimensional space-time as soon as we spatialize time; and we cannot measure time, we cannot even talk about it, without spatializing it.[11] But, in this space-time, time and space remain separate; space can neither disgorge time nor time recede into space. If they bite into one another, in proportions varying with the speed of the system (this is what they do in Einstein's space-time), then we are no longer dealing with anything more than a virtual space-time, that of a physicist imagined as experimenting and no longer that of the physicist who does experiment. For this latter, space-time is at rest, and, in a space-time at rest, time and space remain separate; they intermingle, as we shall see, only in the mixing produced by the system's motion; but the system is in motion only if the physicist who happened to be there abandons it. Now, he cannot abandon it without installing himself in another system; the latter, which is then at rest, will have a space and a time as clearly separated as ours. So that a space that swallows time, and a time that, in turn, absorbs space, are a time or a space always virtual and merely imagined, never real and experienced. It is true that the conception of this space-time will then influence the perception of actual space and time. Across the time and space we had always known to be separate and, for that very reason, structureless, we shall perceive, as through a transparency, an articulated space-time structure. The mathematical notation of these articulations, carried out upon the virtual and brought to its highest level of generality, will give us an unexpected grip on the real. We shall have a powerful means of investigation at hand, a principle of research, which, we can predict, will not henceforth be renounced by the mind of man, even if experiment should impose a new form upon the theory of relativity.

11 This is what we expressed in another form (pp. 57ff.) when we said that science has no way of distinguishing between time unfolding and time unfolded. It spatializes it by the very fact that it measures it.

To show how time and space begin to interweave only when both become fictional, let us return to our system S' and to our observer who, actually located in S', mentally transfers to a different system S, immobilizes it, and then imagines S' endowed with every possible speed. We wish to find out the more special meaning, in the theory of relativity, of the interweaving of space with time considered as an additional dimension. We shall not be changing anything in the outcome and shall be simplifying our exposition, by imagining that the space of systems S and S' has been reduced to a single dimension, a straight line, and that a worm-shaped observer in S' inhabits part of this line. Basically, we are only getting back to the situation prevailing a while back (p. 128). We said that as long as our observer keeps thinking in S' where he is, he purely and simply notes the persistence of length $A'B'$ designated by l. But, as soon as he mentally transfers to S, he forgets the established, concrete invariability of length $A'B'$ or of its square l^2; he conceives it only in abstract form as the invariance of a difference between two squares L^2 and c^2T^2, which would alone be given (calling L the lengthened space $\dfrac{l}{\sqrt{1 - \dfrac{v^2}{c^2}}}$, and T the

interval of time $\dfrac{1}{\sqrt{1 - \dfrac{v^2}{c^2}}} \cdot \dfrac{lv}{c^2}$ which has come to be intercalated

between the two events A' and B', perceived inside system S' as simultaneous). We who know spaces of more than one dimension, have no trouble in geometrically conveying the difference between these two conceptions; for, in the two-dimensional space that for us surrounds line $A'B'$ we have but to erect on the latter a perpendicular $B'C'$ equal to cT, to discern at once that the real observer in S' really perceives side $A'B'$ of the right triangle as invariable, while the fictional observer in S directly perceives (or, rather, conceives) only the other side $B'C'$ and the hypotenuse $A'C'$ of this triangle: line $A'B'$ would then be no more for him than a mental outline by which he completes the triangle, an expression represented by $\sqrt{\overline{A'C'^2} - \overline{B'C'^2}}$. Now, suppose that the wave of a magic wand places our observer, real in S' and fictional in S, in circumstances like ours and allows him to perceive or conceive a space of one more dimension. As a real observer in S', he will perceive the straight line $A'B'$; this is the real. As an imaginary physicist in S, he will perceive or conceive the broken line $A'C'B'$; this is only the virtual; it is the straight line $A'B'$ appearing lengthened and undoubled in the mirror of motion. Now, the straight line $A'B'$ is space. But the broken line $A'C'B'$ is space and time; and so would be an infinity of other broken lines $A'D'B'$, $A'E'B'$, etc., corresponding to different speeds of system S', while line $A'B'$ remains space. These broken, merely virtual, lines of space-time come out of the straight line of space only because of the motion that the mind imparts to the system. They are all subject to the law that the square of their space part, diminished by the square of their time part (we have agreed to make the speed of light our unit of time) leaves a remainder equal to the invariable square of the straight line $A'B'$, the latter a line of pure space, but real. Thus, we see exactly the relation of the space-time amalgam to the separate space and time, which we had always left side by side even though we had made an additional dimension of space out of time by spatializing it. This relation becomes quite striking in the particular case we have chosen by design, the one in which line $A'B'$, perceived by an observer situated in S', joins two events A' and B' given in this system as simultaneous. Here, time and space are so clearly separate that time is eclipsed, leaving only space; a space $A'B'$, this is all that is clearly noted, this is the real. But this reality can be reconstituted virtually by an amalgam of virtual space and virtual time, this space and time lengthening with every increase in the virtual speed imparted to the system by the observer who ideally detaches himself from it. We thus obtain an infinity of merely mental space and time amalgams, all equivalent to space pure and simple, perceived and real.

But, *the essence of the theory of relativity is to rank the real vision with the virtual visions.* The real would be only a special case of the virtual. There would be no difference in kind between the perception of the straight line $A'B'$ in system S', and the conception of the broken line $A'C'B'$, when we imagine ourselves in system S. The straight line $A'B'$ would be a broken line like $A'C'B'$ with a null segment $C'B'$, the value zero assumed here by c^2T^2 being a value like the others. Mathematician and physicist certainly have the right to express themselves in this way. But the philosopher, who must distinguish between the real and the symbolic, will speak differently. He will merely describe what has just happened. There is a real, perceived length $A'B'$. And if we agree to claim only that, considering A' and B' instantaneous and simultaneous, we simply have, by hypothesis, that length of space *plus* a nothing of time. But a motion mentally imparted to the system makes the originally considered space appear time-inflated: l^2 becomes L^2, that is, $l^2 + c^2T^2$. The new space will then have to disgorge time, and L^2 will have to be reduced by c^2T^2 before we can find l^2 again.

We are thus brought back again to our previous conclusions. We were shown that two events, simultaneous for an individual observing them inside his system, are successive for an outsider imagining it in motion. We granted this, but pointed out that despite our giving the name of time to the interval between the two events become successive, it cannot harbor any event. It is, we said, "expanded out of nothing." [12] Here we are witnessing this expansion. For the observer in S', the distance between A' and B' was a length of space l augmented by a zero of time. When the reality l^2 becomes the virtuality L^2, the zero of real time blossoms into a virtual time c^2T^2. But this interval of virtual time is only the nothing of the original time, producing some kind of optical effect in the mirror of motion. Thought can no more lodge even the most fleeting event in it, than we can move a piece of furniture into a room perceived in the depths of a mirror.

But we have been looking at a special case, the one in which the events A' and B' are, from within system S', perceived as

12 See above, p. 106.

simultaneous. This seemed the best way to analyze the operation by which space is added to time, and time to space, in the theory of relativity. Let us now take the more general case in which events A' and B' occur at different moments for the observer in S'. We return to our original notation: we shall call t'_1 the time of event A', and t'_2 that of event B'; we shall designate by $x'_2 - x'_1$ the distance in space from A' to B', x'_2 and x'_1 being the respective distances from A' and from B' to a point of origin O'. To simplify things, we shall again imagine space reduced to a single dimension. But this time we shall ask ourselves how the observer inside S', finding in this system *both* the constancy of the $x'_2 - x'_1$ space length and that of the $t'_2 - t'_1$ time length for any imaginable speed of this system, would picture this constancy when mentally entering a motionless system S. We know [13] that $(x'_2 - x'_1)^2$ would thereupon have to be expanded into

$$\frac{1}{1 - \dfrac{v^2}{c^2}} \left[(x'_2 - x'_1) + v(t'_2 - t'_1) \right]^2$$

a quantity that exceeds $(x'_2 - x'_1)^2$ by

$$\frac{1}{1 - \dfrac{v^2}{c^2}} \left[\frac{v^2}{c^2} (x'_2 - x'_1)^2 + v^2(t'_2 - t'_1)^2 + 2v(x'_2 - x'_1)(t'_2 - t'_1) \right].$$

Here again, as we see, a time would have come to inflate a space.

But, in its turn, a space has been added onto a time, because what was originally $(t'_2 - t'_1)^2$ has become. [14]

$$\frac{1}{1 - \dfrac{v^2}{c^2}} \left[(t'_2 - t'_1) + \frac{v(x'_2 - x'_1)}{c^2} \right]^2$$

a quantity that exceeds $(t'_2 - t'_1)^2$ by

$$\frac{1}{1 - \dfrac{v^2}{c^2}} \left[\frac{v^2}{c^4}(x'_2 - x'_1)^2 + \frac{v^2}{c^2}(t'_2 - t'_1)^2 + \frac{2v}{c^2}(x'_2 - x'_1)(t'_2 - t'_1) \right].$$

The result is that the square of time has been increased by a

13 See p. 130.
14 See p. 131.

quantity which, multiplied by c^2, would give the increase in the square of space. Thus, with space gathering up time and time gathering up space, we see the invariance of the difference $(x_2 - x_1)^2 - c^2(t_2 - t_1)^2$ forming before our very eyes for any assigned speed of the system.

But this amalgam of space and time comes into being for the observer in S' only at the exact instant that he mentally sets the system in motion. And the amalgam exists only in his mind. What is real, that is, observed or observable, is the separate space and time with which he deals in his system. He can associate them in a four-dimensional continuum; this we all do, more or less confusedly, when we spatialize time, and we spatialize it as soon as we measure it. But space and time then remain separately invariant. They amalgamate or, more precisely, their invariance is transferred to the difference $(x_2 - x_1)^2 - c^2(t_2 - t_1)^2$ only for our phantasmal observers. The real observer will offer no objection, for he remains wholly unaffected: as each of his terms $x_2 - x_1$ and $t_2 - t_1$, space interval and time interval, is invariable, from whatever point he considers them inside his system, he abandons them to the phantasmal observer so that the latter may have them enter as he pleases into the expression of his invariant; he adopts this expression beforehand, he knows in advance that it will fit his system as he himself envisages it, for a relation between constant terms is necessarily constant. And much is gained, for the expression with which we provide him is that of a new physical truth: it points out how the "transmission" of light behaves with regard to the "translation" of bodies.

But while it informs him of the relation of the transmission to the translation, it tells him nothing new about space and time; the latter remain what they were, separate from one another, incapable of mingling except as the result of a mathematical fiction intended to symbolize a truth in physics. For this space and time which interpenetrate are not the space and time of any physicist, real or conceived as such. The real physicist makes his measurements in the system in which he finds himself, and which he immobilizes by adopting it as his system of reference; time and space there remain separate and mutually inpenetrable. Space and time interpenetrate in moving systems in which the real physicist does not exist, in which there live only physicists imagined by him—imagined for the greater good of science. But these physicists are not imagined as real or able to be so; to suppose them real, to attribute a consciousness to them, would be to give their system the status of a system of reference, to transport oneself there and become identical with them, to declare that their time and space have ceased to interpenetrate.

We thus return by a long detour to our starting point. We are merely repeating, for space convertible into time and for time reconvertible into space, what we had said about the plurality of times, and about succession and simultaneity considered as interchangeable. And this is quite natural, since we are dealing with the same thing in both cases. The invariance of the expression $dx^2 + dy^2 + dz^2 - c^2dt^2$ follows immediately from the Lorentz equations. And the space-time of Minkowski and Einstein only symbolizes this invariance, as the hypothesis of multiple times and simultaneities convertible into successions only interprets these equations.

Time in Special Relativity and Space in General Relativity

WE ARE now at the end of our study. It had to bear upon time and the paradoxes of time, which we usually associate with the theory of relativity. Hence it is confined to special relativity. Are we therefore left in the abstract? Not at all, nor would we have anything essential to add regarding time, if we introduced a gravitational field into the simplified reality with which we have been occupied until now. Indeed, according to the theory of general relativity, we can no longer either define the synchronization of clocks or declare the speed of light constant in a gravitational field. In all strictness, therefore, the optical definition of time would vanish. As soon as we wish to give meaning to the "time" co-ordinate, we necessarily submit to the conditions of special relativity, going to look for them in the infinite, if necessary.

At each instant, a universe of special relativity is tangent to the universe of general relativity. Moreover, we never have to consider speeds comparable to that of light, or gravitational fields of proportional intensity. Therefore we can in general, in a sufficient approximation, borrow the notion of time in special relativity and retain it just as it stands. In this sense, time is referable to special relativity, as space is to general relativity.

However, the time of special relativity and the space of general relativity are far from having the same degree of reality. A careful study of this point would be singularly instructive for the philosopher. It would bear out the radical distinction that we once drew between the nature of real time and pure space, improperly considered analogous by traditional philosophy. And it would perhaps not be without interest for the physicist. It would reveal that the theory of special relativity and that of general relativity are not animated by exactly the same spirit and do not have quite the same meaning. The first, it must be added, has sprung from a collective effort, while the second reflects Einstein's own genius. The former provides us, above all, with a new formula for results already obtained; it is truly a theory, in the literal sense of the word, a way of viewing. The latter is essentially a method of investigation, an instrument of discovery. But we need not enter into their comparison. Let us merely touch upon the difference between time in one and space in the other. This will be to return to an idea often expressed in the course of the present essay.

When the physicist of general relativity determines the structure of space in general relativity, he is referring to a space in which he is actually located. He checks every proposition he puts forward with appropriate measuring devices. The portion of space whose curvature he describes may be ever so remote: theoretically he would transport himself there, would have us witness the verification of his formula. In short, the space of general relativity presents details that are not merely conceived but could be perceived as well. They relate to the system in which the physicist lives.

But, in the theory of special relativity, the details of time and, more particularly, the plurality of times, do not merely escape, in actual fact, the observation of the physicist who posits them: they are unverifiable in principle. While the space of general relativity is a space in which we exist, the times of special relativity are so defined as to be, all but one, times in which we do not exist. We cannot be in them, because we bring with us, wherever we go, a time that chases out the others, just as a pedestrian's lamp rolls back the fog at each step. We do not even conceive ourselves as being in them, because to enter one of these expanded times mentally would be to adopt the system to which it belongs, to make it our system of reference; at once this time would contract and again become the time that we live inside a system, the time that we have no reason for not believing to be the same in every system.

Expanded and broken-up times are therefore auxiliary times, intercalated by the physicist's mind between the start of his calculations, which is real time, and its finish, which is still this same real time. In the latter we have made the measurements with which we operate; to the latter do the operation's results apply. The others are intermediary between the statement and solution of the problem.

The physicist puts them all on the same plane, gives them the same name, treats them in the same way. And he is justified in this. All are, in fact, measurements of time; and as the measurement of a thing is, in the eyes of the physicist, that very thing, they must all be times for the physicist. But in only one of them—we believe we have demonstrated this—is there succession. Consequently, only one of them endures; the others do not. While the former is a time unquestionably placed back to back with the length that measures it, but is separate from it, the others are only lengths. More precisely, the former is both a time and a "light-line"; the others are only light-lines. But as these last arise from a lengthening of the former, and, as the first was pasted to time, we think of them as lengthened times. Whence comes the infinite number of times in special relativity. This plurality, far from ruling out the oneness of real time, presupposes it.

The paradox begins when we assert that all these times are realities, that is, things perceived or able to be perceived, lived or able to be lived. We had implicitly assumed the opposite for all of them—except one—when we had identified time with the light-line. Such is the contradiction that our mind divines, even when it does not perceive it clearly. Nor, it must be added, is it attributable to any physicist as such: it arises only in a physics posing as a metaphysics. To this contradiction our mind cannot adjust. We have been wrong to attribute its resistance to a prejudice of common sense. Prejudices vanish or at least weaken upon reflection. But, in the present case,

reflection strengthens our conviction and even ends by render-
ing it unshakable, because it reveals in the times of special
relativity—one among them excepted—times without duration,
in which events cannot succeed each other, nor things subsist,
nor beings age.

Aging and duration belong to the order of quality. No work
of analysis can resolve them into pure quantity. Here the thing
remains separate from its measurement, which besides, bears
upon a space representative of time rather than upon time
itself. But it is quite otherwise with space. Its measurement
exhausts its essence. This time, the details discovered and described by physics belong to the thing and no longer to a
mental view of it. Let us rather say, they are reality itself; the
thing is, this time, *relation*. Descartes reduced matter—considered at the instant—to extension; physics, in his eyes, attained
to the real insofar as it was geometrical. A study of general
relativity, parallel to the one we have made of special relativity,
would show that the reduction of gravitation to inertia has
justly been an elimination of ready-made concepts which,
coming between the physicist and his object, between the mind
and the relations constitutive of the thing, was at this point
preventing physics from being a geometry. In this respect, Einstein is the continuator of Descartes.

APPENDIXES TO THE SECOND EDITION

APPENDIX I

The Journey in the Projectile

WE HAVE stated but cannot repeat often enough: in the theory
of relativity, the slowing of clocks is only as real as the shrinking of objects by distance. The shrinking of receding objects
is the way the eye takes note of their recession. The slowing
of the clock in motion is the way the theory of relativity takes
note of its motion: this slowing measures the difference, or
"distance," in speed between the speed of the moving system
to which the clock is attached and the speed, assumed to be
zero, of the system of reference, which is motionless by definition; it is a perspective effect. Just as upon reaching a distant
object we see it in its true size and then see shrink the object
we have just left, so the physicist, going from system to system,
will always find the same real time in the systems in which he
installs himself and which, by that very fact, he immobilizes,
but will always, in keeping with the perspective of relativity,
have to attribute more or less slowed times to the systems
which he vacates, and which, by that very fact, he sets in motion at greater or lesser speeds. Now, if I reasoned about someone far away, whom distance has reduced to the size of a
midget, as about a genuine midget, that is, as about someone
who is and acts like a midget, I would end in paradoxes or
contradictions; as a midget, he is "phantasmal," the shortening
of his figure being only an indication of his distance from me.
No less paradoxical will be the results if I give to the wholly
ideal, phantasmal clock that tells time in the moving system
in the perspective of relativity, the status of a real clock telling
this time to a real observer. My distantly-removed individuals
are real enough and, as real, retain their size; it is as midgets
that they are phantasmal. In the same way, the clocks that

163

shift with respect to motionless me are indeed real clocks; but insofar as they are real, they run like mine and tell the same time as mine; it is insofar as they run more slowly and tell a different time that they become phantasmal, like people who have degenerated into midgets.

Let us imagine a normal-sized Peter and Paul conversing. Peter stays where he is, next to me; I see him and he sees himself in his true size. But Paul moves off and becomes midget-sized in Peter's eyes and mine. If I now go around thinking of Peter as normal-sized and of Paul as a midget, picturing him that way back with Peter and resuming his conversation, I shall necessarily end in absurdities or paradoxes; I have no right to bring Peter, who has remained normal, in contact with Paul turned midget, to imagine that the latter can speak with the former, see him, listen to him, perform any action at all, because Paul, as midget, is only a mental view, an image, a phantom. Nevertheless, this is exactly what both partisan and adversary of the theory of relativity did in the debate, begun at the Collège de France in April 1922, on the implications of special relativity.[1] The former merely kept pointing to the perfect mathematical coherence of the theory, but then retained the paradox of multiple and real times—as if one were to say that Paul, having returned to the vicinity of Peter, had been changed into a midget. The latter probably wanted no paradox, but he could have avoided it only by showing that Peter is a real being and that Paul turned midget is a mere phantom, that is, by making a distinction that belongs no longer to mathematical physics but to philosophy. Remaining, on the contrary, on his opponents' ground, he only succeeded in furnishing them with an occasion for reinforcing their position and confirming the paradox. The truth is that the paradox vanishes when we make the distinction that is indispensable. The theory of relativity remains intact, with its infinite multiplicity of imaginary times and a single, real time.

This is exactly our argument. That there has been some

[1] We are alluding to an objection to the theory of relativity voiced by M. Painlevé.

difficulty in grasping it, and that it is not always easy, even for the relativist physicist, to philosophize in terms of relativity, is to be gathered from a very interesting letter addressed to us by a most distinguished physicist.[2] Inasmuch as other readers may have encountered the same difficulty and as none, surely, will have formulated it more clearly, we are going to quote the main points in this letter. We shall then reproduce our reply.

Let AB be the trajectory of the projectile plotted in the system earth. Starting from point A on the earth, where Peter will remain, the projectile carrying Paul heads toward B at speed v; having arrived at B, the projectile turns around and heads back to point A at speed $-v$. Peter and Paul meet again, compare measurements, and exchange impressions. I say that they are not in agreement about the duration of the journey: if Peter asserts that Paul has stayed away a given length of time, which he has estimated at A, Paul will reply that he is quite sure he has not spent that much time on the trip, because he has himself calculated its duration with a unit of time defined in the same way and has found it shorter. Both will be right.

I am assuming that the trajectory has been staked out with identical clocks, borne along with the earth, hence belonging to the system earth, and that they have been synchronized by light signals. In the course of his journey, Paul can read the time shown by the particular clock near which he is passing, and can compare this time with that indicated by an identical clock in his projectile.

You can already see how I am orienting the question: the point is to compare adjacent events, to observe a simultaneity of clock readings *at the same place*. We are not straying from the psychological conception of simultaneity, for, in accord with your own expression, an event E occurring beside clock C is given in simultaneity with a reading on clock C in the psychologist's sense of the word simultaneity.

At the event "departure of the projectile," Peter's and Paul's clocks both point to 0°. I am assuming, of course, that the projectile attains its speed instantaneously. There, then, is the projectile that constitutes a system S' traveling in rectilinear and uniform motion

2 [Bergson tactfully refrains from naming this physicist, but he is identified as Jean Becquerel (1878–1953) by André Metz in "Le temps d'Einstein et la nouvelle édition de l'ouvrage de M. Bergson, *Durée et simultanéité*," *Revue de philosophie*, XXXI (1924), 241–260.]

with respect to the system earth, at speed v. For the sake of clarity, I shall assume that $v = 259,807$ km/sec., so that the factor $\sqrt{1 - \dfrac{v^2}{c^2}}$ equals $\dfrac{1}{2}$.

I shall assume that at the end of an hour, recorded on the clock of the projectile, the latter passes the middle M of the distance AB. Paul reads the time both on his clock (1^e) and, simultaneously, on the system earth's clock located at M. What time will he read on the latter? One of the Lorentz equations supplies the answer.

We know that the Lorentz formulae give the relations linking the space and time co-ordinates of an event *measured by Peter* with the space and time co-ordinates of the same event *measured by Paul*. In the present case, the event is the meeting of the projectile with the system earth's clock at M; its co-ordinates in the projectile system S' are $x' = 0$, $t' = 1^e$; the formula $t = \dfrac{1}{\sqrt{1 - \dfrac{v^2}{c^2}}}\left(t' + \dfrac{vx'}{c^2}\right)$ gives $t = 2t'$ (since $\dfrac{1}{\sqrt{1 - \dfrac{v^2}{c^2}}} = 2$). The clock at point M therefore records 2^e.

Paul therefore notes that the system earth's clock before which he is passing is one hour ahead of his; of course, he does not have to push his clock ahead; he records the disagreement. Continuing on his journey, he notes that the time differences between his clock and those he successively encounters increase in such proportion to his own clock-time that, on arriving at B, his clock points to 2^e; but the system earth's clock at B points to 4^e.

Having arrived at B, the projectile turns back along BA at speed $-v$. Now there is a *change in system of reference*. Paul abruptly leaves the system moving with speed $+v$ with respect to the earth and passes into the system of speed $-v$. Everything starts over again on the return trip. Let us imagine that the clock in the projectile and the one at B are automatically moved back to zero, and that the other earth-linked clocks are synchronized with the one at B. We can begin the preceding argument all over again: at the end of one hour's journey, recorded on Paul's clock, he will again find as he passes M that his clock reads 1^e, whereas the earth clock reads 2^e, etc.

But why imagine the clocks set back to zero? It was useless to interfere with them. We know there is an initial shifting from zero to take into account; this shifting amounts to 2^e for the projectile's clock and 4^e for the system earth's clock; they are constants to be added to the times that would be shown had all the clocks been pushed back to zero. Thus, if we have not interfered with the clocks, when the projectile recrosses M, Paul's clock will show $1 + 2 = 3^e$, the one at point M, $2 + 4 = 6^e$, and Peter's $4 + 4 = 8^e$.

Behold the result! For Peter, who has remained at A on the earth, it is indeed eight hours that have elapsed between Paul's departure and return. But, if we ask "living, conscious" Paul, he will say that his clock read 0^e at departure and reads 4^e upon return, that it has recorded a duration of 4^e, and that he has really been traveling 4^e and not 8^e.

So goes the objection. As we stated, it is impossible to present it in clearer terms. That is why we have reproduced it just as it was addressed to us, without reformulation. Here, then is our reply:

"Two important remarks must be made at the outset.

1. If we take a stand outside the theory of relativity, we conceive of absolute motion and, therewith, absolute immobility; there will be really motionless systems in the universe. But, if we assume that all motion is relative, what becomes of immobility? It will be the state of the system of reference, the system in which the physicist imagines himself located, inside which he is seen taking measurements and to which he relates every point in the universe. One cannot move with respect to oneself; and, consequently, the physicist-builder of Science, is motionless by definition, once the theory of relativity is accepted. It unquestionably occurs to the relativist physicist, as to any other physicist, to set in motion the system of reference in which he had at first installed himself; but then, willy-nilly, consciously or unconsciously, he adopts another, if only for an instant; he locates his real personality within this new system, which thus becomes motionless by definition; and it is then no more than an image of himself that he mentally perceives in what was just now, in what will in a moment again become, his system of reference.

2. If we stand outside the theory of relativity, we can quite readily conceive of an absolutely motionless individual, Peter, at point A, next to an absolutely motionless cannon; we can also conceive of an individual, Paul, inside a projectile

launched far out from Peter, moving in a straight line with absolutely uniform motion toward point B and then returning, still in a straight line with absolutely uniform motion, to point A. But, from the standpoint of the theory of relativity, there is no longer any absolute motion or absolute immobility. The first of the two phases just mentioned then becomes simply an increasing distance apart between Peter and Paul; and the second, a decreasing one. We can therefore say, at will, that Paul is moving away from and then drawing closer to Peter, or that Peter is moving away from and then drawing closer to Paul. If I am with Peter, who then chooses himself as system of reference, it is Peter who is motionless; and I explain the gradual widening of the gap by saying that the projectile is leaving the cannon, and the gradual narrowing, by saying that the projectile is returning to it. If I am with Paul, now adopting himself as system of reference, I explain the widening and narrowing by saying that it is Peter, together with the cannon and the earth, who is leaving and then returning to Paul. The symmetry is perfect.[3] We are dealing, in short, with two systems, S and S', which nothing prevents us from assuming to be identical; and one sees that since Peter and Paul regard themselves, each respectively, as a system of reference and are thereby immobilized, their situations are interchangeable.

I come now to the essential point.

If we stand outside the theory of relativity, there is no objection to expressing ourselves like anyone else, to saying that both Peter and Paul, the one absolutely motionless and the other absolutely in motion, exist at the same time as conscious beings, even physicists. But, from the standpoint of the theory of relativity, immobility is of our decreeing: that system becomes immobile which we enter mentally. A "living, conscious" physicist then exists in it by hypothesis. In short, Peter

---

[3] It is perfect, we repeat, between Peter and Paul as the referrers, as it is between Peter and Paul as the referents. Paul's turning back has nothing to do with the matter, since Peter turns back as well if Paul is the referrer. We shall, moreover, directly demonstrate the reciprocity of acceleration in the next two appendixes.

is a physicist, a living, conscious being. But what of Paul? If I leave him living and conscious, all the more if I make him a physicist like Peter, I thereupon imagine him taking himself as system of reference, I immobilize him. But Peter and Paul cannot both be motionless at one and the same time, since, by hypothesis, there is first a steadily increasing and then a steadily decreasing distance between them. I must therefore choose between them; and, in point of fact, I did choose, since I said that it was Paul who was shot into space and thereby immobilized Peter's system into a system of reference.[4] But then, Paul is clearly a living, conscious being at the moment of leaving Peter; he is still clearly a living, conscious being at the moment of returning to Peter (he would even remain a living, conscious being in the interval if, during this interval, we agreed to lay aside all questions of measurement and, more especially, all relativist physics); but, for Peter the physicist, making measurements and reasoning about them, accepting the laws of physicomathematical perspective, Paul, once launched into space, is no more than a mental view, an image—what I have called a "phantom" or, again, an "empty puppet." It is this Paul en route (neither conscious nor living, reduced to the state of an image) who exists in a slower time than Peter's. It would therefore be useless for Peter, attached to the motionless system that we call earth, to try to question this particular Paul at the moment of his re-entering the system, about his travel impressions: this Paul has noted nothing and had no impressions, since he exists only in Peter's mind. What is more, he vanishes the moment he touches Peter's system. The Paul who has impressions is a Paul who has lived in the interval, and the Paul who has lived in the interval is a Paul who was interchangeable with Peter at every moment, who occupied a time

4 It is clearly by extension that use has been made of the expression "system of reference" in the passage from the above-quoted letter, in which it was stated that Paul, in turning back, "changes his system of reference." Paul is really, by turns, in systems that *can become* systems of reference; but neither of these two systems, while it is considered in motion, is a system of reference. See Appendix III, particularly footnote 4 on pp. 184–185.

identical with Peter's and aged just as much as Peter. Everything the physicist will tell us about Paul's findings on his
journey will have to be understood as being about findings
that *the physicist Peter attributes to Paul* when he makes himself a referrer and considers Paul no more than a referent—
findings that Peter is obliged to attribute to Paul as soon as he
seeks a picture of the world that is independent of any system
of reference. The Paul who gets out of the projectile on returning from his journey and then again becomes part of
Peter's system, is something like a flesh-and-blood person step-
ping out of the canvas upon which he had been painted: it
was to the portrait, not the person, to Paul referent, not referrer, that Peter's arguments and calculations applied while
Paul was on his journey. The person replaces the portrait,
Paul referent again becomes Paul referrer or capable of referring, the moment he passes from motion to immobility.

But I must go into more detail, as you yourself have done.
You imagine the projectile impelled by speed v such that we
have $\sqrt{1 - \dfrac{v^2}{c^2}} = \dfrac{1}{2}$. Let AB then be the trajectory of the projectile plotted in the system earth, and M the middle of the
straight line AB. "I shall assume," you say, "that at the end
of an hour recorded on the clock in the projectile, the latter
passes the middle M of the distance AB. Paul reads the time
both on his clock (1^e) and, simultaneously, on the system
earth's clock located at M. What time will he read on the
latter, if both clocks pointed to 0^e at departure? One of the
Lorentz equations gives the answer: the clock at M points
to 2^e."

I reply: Paul is incapable of reading anything at all; for,
insofar as, according to you, he is in motion with respect to
motionless Peter, whom you have made referrer, he is nothing
more than a blank image, a mental view. Peter alone will
henceforth have to be treated as a real, conscious being (unless
you renounce the physicist's standpoint, which here is one of
measurement, to return to the standpoint of common sense or

ordinary perception). Hence we must not say, "Paul reads the time. . . ." We must say, "Peter, that is, the physicist, pictures Paul reading the time. . . ." And, since Peter applies, and must apply, the Lorentz equations, he naturally pictures Paul reading 1ᵉ on his moving clock at the moment when, in Peter's view, this clock passes in front of the clock of the motionless system, which, in Peter's eyes, points to 2ᵉ. But, you will tell me: "Nonetheless, does there not exist in the moving system, a moving clock that records its own particular time independently of anything Peter can imagine of it?" Without any doubt. The time of this real clock is exactly what Paul would read on it if he became real again, I mean, alive and conscious. But, at this precise moment, Paul would become the physicist; he would take his system as the system of reference and immobilize it. His clock would then point to 2ᵉ—exactly the time to which Peter's clock pointed. I use the past tense because already Peter's clock no longer points to 2ᵉ but to 1ᵉ, being now the clock of Peter referent and no longer referrer.

I need not pursue the argument. Everything you said about the times read by Paul on his clock when he arrives at *B*, then when he comes back to *M*, and, finally, when he is about to touch *A* and re-enter the system earth, all this applies not to living, conscious Paul, actually looking at his moving clock, but to a Paul whom physicist Peter *pictures as watching* this clock (and whom the physicist *must* picture in this way and need not distinguish from a living, conscious Paul: this distinction is the philosopher's concern). It is for this merely imagined and referred-to Paul that four—imagined—hours will have elapsed while eight—lived—hours will have elapsed for Peter. But Paul, conscious and therefore referrer, will have lived eight hours, since we shall have to apply to him everything we just said about Peter."

To sum up, in this reply we once more gave the meaning of the Lorentz equations. We have described this meaning in many ways; we have sought by many means to present a concrete vision of it. One could just as easily have established it *in abstracto* in the standard step-by-step deduction of these equations.[5] One would recognize that the Lorentz equations quite clearly express what the measurements *attributed* to S' must be in order that the physicist in S may see the physicist *imagined by him* in S', finding the same speed for light as he does.

[5] Albert Einstein, *La théorie de la relativité restreinte et generalisée,* pp. 101–107; Jean Becquerel, *Le principe de relativité et la théorie de la gravitation,* pp. 29–33.

The Reciprocity of Acceleration

IN THE preceding Appendix, as in our fourth chapter, we broke down the journey in the projectile into two journeys in opposite directions, both of which were uniform translations. There was no point in bringing up the difficulties that attach, or seem to attach, to the idea of acceleration: in the course of this work, we have never declared for reciprocity anywhere except in the case of uniform motion, where it is obvious. But we could just as well have taken into account the acceleration that the change of direction gives rise to and then have considered the entire journey in the projectile as a variable motion. Our argument would have held, for we shall see that acceleration is itself reciprocal and that the two systems S and S' are entirely interchangeable.

One sometimes hesitates to admit this reciprocity of acceleration for certain special reasons, which will concern us in the next Appendix, when we shall be dealing with "World-lines." But one also hesitates because, as it is usually stated, accelerated motion in a moving system is conveyed by phenomena that do not occur symmetrically in the system ruled motionless, which has been taken as the system of reference. In dealing with a train moving on a track, one agrees to speak of reciprocity as long as the motion remains uniform: the translation, it is thought, can be attributed equally to the track or to the train; all that the motionless physicist on the track asserts about the moving train could as well be asserted about the track, which has become mobile by the physicist's getting onto the train. But let the speed of the train increase or decrease abruptly, let it stop: the physicist inside the train feels a jolt, and this jolt has no counterpart on the track. Hence, no more reciprocity in the case of acceleration; the latter manifests itself in phenomena at least some of which concern only one of the two systems.

There is a grave confusion here, whose causes and effects it would be interesting to probe. Let us limit ourselves to describing its nature. *One continues to see a single system in what has just been revealed as a collection of systems, a manifold of different systems.*

To be immediately persuaded of this, we have only to render the two systems under consideration actually indecomposable by making, say, two physical points out of them. It is clear that if point S' is in variable rectilinear motion with respect to S ruled motionless, S will have a variable rectilinear motion of the same speed at the same moment with respect to S' ruled motionless in its turn.[1] But we can just as readily attribute to S and S' any dimension and any motion of translation we like: if we adhere to our hypothesis, namely, that each of the two is and remains a system, that is, a group of points compelled constantly to keep the same relative positions with respect to one another, and if we agree to consider only translations,[2] it is obvious that we shall be able to treat them as if they were two physical points, and that their acceleration will be reciprocal.

To these systems S and S' in any state of reciprocal translation whatever, there will moreover apply, as far as time is concerned, everything we said about reciprocal motion when it was uniform. Let S be the system of reference: S' will have changing speeds, each of which will be kept up for finite or

[1] It would be inaccurate, moreover, to say that these speeds are in opposite directions. To attribute speed in opposite directions to two systems would consist, at bottom, of mentally settling in a third system of reference, when we have given ourselves only S and S'. Let us rather say that the direction of speed will have to be described in the same way in both cases because whether we adopt S as system of reference or whether we prefer taking our place in S', in both cases the motion we attribute from there to the other system is a motion that brings the mobile nearer or sends it farther away. In a word, the two systems are interchangeable and whatever we say in S about S' can be repeated in S' about S.

[2] The case of rotation will be examined in the next Appendix.

infinitely short periods; to each of these motions the Lorentz formulae will, of course, apply; and we shall obtain, either by an addition of finite parts or by an integration of infinitely small elements, the time t' which is judged to elapse in S' while time t is elapsing in S. Here again, t' will be smaller than t; here again, there will have been an expansion of the second and a slowing of time as a result of motion. But here again the shorter time will be merely attributed time, incapable of being lived, unreal: only, the time of S will be a time that could be lived, a time that is, moreover, actually so lived, a real time. Now, if we take S' as our system of reference, it is in S' that this same real time will elapse and into S that the imaginary time t' will be transferred. In a word, if there is reciprocity in the case of accelerated motion, as in that of uniform motion, the slowing of time for the system assumed in motion will be figured the same way in both cases, a slowing again only imagined and not affecting real time.

The symmetry between S and S' is therefore perfect, insofar as S and S' are really two systems.

But, without noticing it, we sometimes substitute for the system ruled in motion a number of separate systems endowed with different motions, which we nevertheless continue to treat as a single system. We often do this even when we speak of phenomena "inside the system" which occur as the result of this system's accelerated motion and when, for example, we are shown a passenger jolted in his seat by the train's sudden stop. If the passenger is shaken up, it is clearly because the physical points of which his body is composed do not maintain unchanging positions with respect to the train, nor, in general, with respect to one another. They therefore do not form a single system with the train, or even among themselves—as many systems S'', and S''', etc., are revealed by the "jolt" as are endowed with motions of their own. Consequently, in the eyes of the physicist in S, they have their own times t'', t''', etc. The reciprocity is, moreover, still complete between S and S'', and between S and S''', as between S and S'. If we install the real physicist, by turns, in S'', S''', etc. (he cannot be in several at the same time), he will find and live the same real time t in each, in that event successively attributing the merely conceived times t'', t''', etc., to system S. This means that the passenger's jolt introduces no asymmetry.[3] From the standpoint we have to assume, it is dissolved into perfectly reciprocal manifestations affecting the invariable point-systems with which we are dealing. The standpoint we must assume is, in fact, that of the measurement of time in the theory of relativity, and the clocks of which this theory speaks can clearly be likened to ordinary physical points, since their sizes are never taken into account. It is, therefore, really ordinary physical points that are in motion, in the case of accelerated as in that of uniform motion, when we compare the times of these reciprocally moving clocks in the theory of relativity. In short, it matters little whether the motion is uniform or variable: there will always be reciprocity between the two systems that we bring face to face.

This, moreover, is what we are about to see with more precision in the next Appendix, where we shall consider the reciprocity of acceleration in all its generality. The points M_1 and M_2 with which we shall first deal can be considered clocks as well.

---

[3] Here, as elsewhere, we must remember that science retains, and must retain, only the visual aspect of motion. The theory of relativity requires before all, as we have shown (pp. 32ff), that we apply this principle with utmost rigor. We sometimes forget this when we speak of the jolt felt by our passenger. Whoever wishes to think in terms of relativity must begin by either eliminating the tactile or transposing it into the visual. If we resolve the jolt into its visual elements, and if we keep in mind the meaning of the word "system," the reciprocity of acceleration again becomes apparent. We must, moreover, guard against the temptation mentally to enter systems S'', S''', etc., *at the same time*. We do this when we speak of the jolt—even reduced to what we *see* of it, as of a single fact. We must, indeed, distinguish between the point of view of perception and that of science. Perception undoubtedly embraces S'', S''', etc., all at one time. But the physicist cannot adopt them *in the ensemble* as a system of reference: he must select one of them, considering them *one at a time*.

"Proper-Time" and "World-Line"

WE HAVE just demonstrated the reciprocity of acceleration, first in a particular case, then in a more general way. It is natural for this reciprocity to escape our attention when the theory of relativity is presented in its mathematical form. We implied the reason for this in our sixth chapter,[1] where we stated (1) that the theory of relativity is obliged to rank the "real vision" with the "virtual vision," the measurement actually made by an existing physicist with the one considered made by a merely imagined physicist; (2) that the form given this theory since Minkowski has precisely the effect of hiding the difference between the real and the virtual, between what is perceived, or perceptible, and what is not. The reciprocity of acceleration appears only if we restore this distinction, secondary for the physicist, fundamental for the philosopher. At the same time the meaning of the "slowing" that acceleration imparts to a moving clock is realized. It is realized without there being anything to add to what we said when treating of uniform motion: acceleration cannot create new conditions here, since one must still apply the Lorentz formulae (in general, to infinitesimal elements) when one speaks of multiple, slowed times. But, for greater precision, we are going to examine in detail the special form which the theory of relativity exhibits in this case. We take it from a recent book that is already a classic, the important work of Jean Becquerel (*Le principe de relativité et la théorie de la gravitation* [Paris: Gauthier-Villars Cie, 1922], pp. 48–51).

In a system of reference connected with a portion of matter, that

1 Particularly pp. 131ff., and pp. 152ff.

177

is, in a system all of whose points are in the same state of motion, any motion, as this portion of matter, the spatial distance between two events relating to this portion of matter is always zero. We therefore have, in this system in which $dx = dy = dz = 0$,

$$ds = cd\tau, \quad \int_A^B ds = c \int_A^B d\tau,$$

$d\tau$ is *the proper-time element* of the portion of matter considered and of the whole system connected with it. The proper-time $\int_A^B d\tau$

elapsed *between two events* A *and* B *is the time an observer will compute, the time that the clocks in the system will record.*

A clock attached to a mobile (whose motion need now no longer be subject to the restriction of uniform translation) *computes the length, divided by* c, *of the arc of the World-line of this mobile.*

Let us now consider a *free* physical point M_1. Galileo's law of inertia informs us that this point is in rectilinear, uniform motion: to this *state of motion* there corresponds, in space-time, a *"World-line"* formed by the block of events that represent the different, successive positions of this mobile in its state of uniform motion, positions that we can plot in any system at all.

On the World-line of M_1 let us pick out two determinate events A and B. . . . Between these events we can imagine an infinite number of real World-lines in space-time. . . . Let us consider any one of these World-lines; to do this, we need only contemplate a second mobile M_2 which, after leaving event A and traversing a longer or shorter spatial distance at a greater or lesser speed, a distance we shall plot in a system in uniform translation connected with M_1, rejoins this mobile M_1 at event B.

To sum up, our data are as follows: the two mobiles M_1 and M_2 are in absolute coincidence at events A and B; between these events their World-lines differ; M_1 is assumed in uniform translation. Finally, we plot the events in a system S connected with M_1.

It is important to observe that M_2, having left the uniform system S at A to return to it at B (or only to pass out of it at B), has necessarily undergone an acceleration between events A and B.

Let us take two points of time t and $t + dt$ in system S, included between t_A and t_B at which events A and B occur, always in system S connected with M_1. At the points of time t and $t + dt$, the second mobile M_2 is referenced x, y, z, t and $x + dx$, $y + dy$, $z + dz$, $t + dt$ in system S; these co-ordinates locate, on the World-line of M_2, two infinitely adjacent events C and D, whose interval is ds; we have [2]

[2] The expression of the constant is most often written this way (rather than in the manner adopted in the present work), in order to keep S^2

$ds^2 = -dx^2 - dy^2 - dz^2 + c^2dt^2$. But we also have $ds = cd\tau$, $d\tau$ being the element of proper-time of the mobile M_2. From this, we deduce [3]

$$ds^2 = c^2d\tau^2 = c^2dt^2 \left\{ 1 - \frac{1}{c^2}\left[\left(\frac{dx}{dt}\right)^2 + \left(\frac{dy}{dt}\right)^2 + \left(\frac{dz}{dt}\right)^2 \right] \right\}$$

$$= c^2dt^2 \left(1 - \frac{v^2}{c^2} \right) = a^2c^2dt^2$$

v being the speed of the mobile M_2 at the point of time t, both speed and time being computed in the uniform system of mobile M_1.

We therefore finally have

(1) $$d\tau = adt,$$

which means: *the proper-time of a mobile* M_2 *between two events on its World-line is shorter than the time computed between the same events in a system in uniform translation; it is as much shorter as the speed of the mobile with respect to the uniform system is greater.* . . .

We have not yet taken note of the absolute coincidence of mobiles M_1 (in uniform translation) and M_2 (any motion), at events A and B. Let us integrate (1)

$$\int_A^B d\tau = \int_{t_A}^{t_B} adt,$$

the more the motion of the mobile M_2 *between events* A *and* B *common to the two moving points differs from a rectilinear, uniform motion*, the greater will be its speeds with respect to M_1, since the total duration $t_B - t_A$ is fixed, and *the shorter the total proper-time will be*.

In other words: *between two determinate events, the* LONGER *World-line is the one corresponding to the motion of uniform translation.*

[It is important to observe that, in the preceding demonstration, there is no reciprocity between the systems of reference connected with M_1 and M_2, because M_2 is not in uniform translation. The acceleration of M_2 has created the asymmetry: here one recognizes the absolute character of acceleration.]

---

from being negative, as would happen in the most frequent case, that in which the distances between two events in space is shorter than the path traversed by light during the interval of time that separates them. This case is the only one in which, according to the theory of relativity, one of the two events can act upon the other. This is precisely the hypothesis that is assumed above.

[3] The factor $\sqrt{1 - \dfrac{v^2}{c^2}}$ is here designated by a.

Strange consequences follow from the results just established.

In a system in uniform translation—the earth, for example, because its acceleration is slight—two identical, synchronized clocks are at the same spot. We shift one very rapidly and bring it back again close to the other at the end of time t (the time of the system); it is found to be behind the other clock by $t - \int_0^t a\,dt$; if its acceleration was instantaneous at departure as upon arrival and its speed has remained constant, the slowing amounts to $t(1 - a)$.

No one could express himself with greater precision. Moreover, from the physico-mathematical standpoint, the argument is irreproachable: the physicist ranks the measurements actually made in one system with those which, from this system, *appear as if* actually made in another. It is out of these two kinds of measurement, merged in the same treatment, that he constructs a scientific world-view; and, as he must treat them in the same way, he gives them the same meaning. Quite different is the philosopher's role. In a general way, he wants to distinguish the real from the symbolic; more exactly and more particularly, for him, the question here is to determine which is the time lived or capable of being lived, the time actually computed, and which is the time merely imagined, the time which would vanish at the very instant that a flesh-and-blood observer would betake himself to the spot in order to compute it in actuality. From this new point of view, comparing only the real with the real, or else, the imagined with the imagined, we see complete reciprocity reappearing, there where acceleration seemed to have brought on asymmetry. But let us closely examine the text we just quoted.

We notice that the system of reference is defined there as "a system all of whose points are in the same state of motion." The fact is that the "system of reference connected with M" is assumed in uniform motion, while the "system of reference connected with M_2" is in a state of variable motion. Let S and S' be these two systems. It is clear that the real physicist then gives himself a third system S'' in which he imagines himself installed and which is thereby immobilized; only with respect to this system can S and S' be in motion. If there were only S and S', he would necessarily place himself in S or in S', and necessarily one of the two systems would be found immobilized. But, the real physicist being in S'', the real time, that is, the lived and actually measured time, is the one in system S''. The time of system S, being the time of a system in motion with respect to S'', now becomes a slowed time; it is, moreover, only an imagined time, that is, *attributed* to system S by the observer in S''. In this S system an observer has been imagined who takes it as his system of reference. But, once again, if the physicist really took this system as his system of reference, he would be placing himself within it, he would be immobilizing it; since he remains in S'' and leaves system S in motion, he is limited to *picturing an observer* taking S as system of reference. In short, we have in S what we called a phantom observer, judged to be taking as his system of reference this S system that the real physicist in S'' pictures in motion.

Moreover, between the observer in S (*if he became real*) and the real observer in S'' the reciprocity is perfect. The phantom observer in S, turned real again, would immediately rediscover the real time of system S'', since his system would be immobilized, since the real physicist would have transported himself to it, since the two systems, as referrers, are interchangeable. The phantasmal time would now be elapsing in S''.

Now, everything we just said about S with respect to S'' we can repeat for system S' with respect to this same S'' system. Real time, lived and actually computed by the physicist in S'' will again be present in motionless S''. This physicist, taking his system as system of reference will attribute to S' a slowed time, one which is now of variable rhythm, since the speed of the system varies. Moreover, at each instant, there will again be reciprocity between S'' and S'; if the observer in S'' were to transport himself into S', the latter would at once be immobilized and all the accelerations that were present in S' would pass into S''; the slowed, merely *attributed* times would pass with them into S'', and it is in S' that time would be real.

We have just considered the relation of motionless S'' to S in uniform translation, then the relation of motionless S'' to S' in a state of variable motion. There is complete reciprocity in both cases—provided we consider both the systems we are comparing as either referrers, when entering them one at a time, or as referents when leaving them one at a time. In both cases there is a single, real time, the one which the real physicist first noted in S'' and finds again in S and S' when he transports himself into them, since S and S'' are interchangeable as referrers, as are also S' and S''.

It remains then to consider directly the relation of S in uniform translation to S' in variable motion. Now we know that if S is in motion, the physicist who is found in it is a merely imagined physicist—the real physicist is in S''. The system of reference really adopted is S'', and the system S is not a real system of reference but an imagined system of reference that a merely imagined observer adopts. This observer is already phantasmal. Doubly phantasmal then is his noting of what is happening in S'; it is a mental view attributed to an observer who is himself only a mental view. Thus, when it is stated, in the above-mentioned text, that there is asymmetry between S and S', it is clear that this asymmetry does not concern measurements really taken in either S or S', but those which *are attributed* to the observer in S from the standpoint of S'', and those which, still from the standpoint of S'', *are considered to be attributed* by the observer in S to the observer in S'. But, in that case, what is the true relation between the real S and the real S'?

To discover it, we have only to place our real observer in S and S' by turns. Our two systems will thus become successively real, but also successively motionless. We could, moreover, have taken this path right away without passing through such a long detour, by following the quoted text to the letter and considering only the special case in which system S, which we are told is in uniform motion, moves at a constant speed of zero. Here, then, is our real observer in S, now motionless. It is clear that this observer in S will discover that there is no reciprocity between his own motionless system and system S' which leaves it to rejoin it later. But, if we place him now in S', which will thus be found immobilized, he will note that the relation of S to S' is just what the relation of S' to S was a moment ago: it is now S which leaves S' and which has just rejoined it. Thus, there is symmetry once again, complete reciprocity between S and S', referrer, and S' and S, referent. Acceleration therefore changes nothing in the situation; in the case of variable motion, as in that of uniform motion, the rhythm of time varies from one system to another only if one of the two systems is referrer and the other, referent, that is, if one of the two times is capable of being lived, is actually computed, is real, while the other is incapable of being lived, is merely conceived as computed, is unreal. In the case of variable motion as in that of uniform motion, asymmetry exists not between the two systems but between one of the systems and a mental view of the other. It is true that the quoted text clearly shows us the impossibility of mathematically expressing this distinction in the theory of relativity. The consideration of "World-lines" introduced by Minkowski even has as its essence the masking or rather the wiping out of the difference between the real and the imagined. An expression like $ds^2 = -dx^2 - dy^2 - dz^2 + c^2dt^2$ seems to place us outside every system of reference, in the Absolute, in the presence of an entity comparable to the Platonic Idea. Then, when we apply it to specific systems of reference, we think we are particularizing and materializing an immaterial, universal essence, as the Platonist does when he descends from the pure Idea, containing immanently all the individuals of a genus, to any one among them. All systems then acquire equal rank; all assume the same value; the one in which we have $dx = dy = dz = 0$ becomes just another system. We forget that this system harbored the real physicist, that the others are only those of imagined physicists, that we had been looking for a mode of representation suitable to the latter and the former at the same time, and that the expression $ds^2 = -dx^2 - dy^2 - dz^2 + c^2dt^2$ had been precisely the result of that search. It is therefore truly begging the question to hold up this general expression as authority for equating every system and declaring all times of equal worth, since this community of expression was obtained only by neglecting the difference between the time in one of them— the only verified or verifiable, the only real time—and the merely imagined, fictional times in all the others. The physicist had the right to wipe out this difference. But the philosopher must re-establish it. This is what we have done.[4]

[4] In a word, the theory of relativity requires that the physicist be installed in one of the systems he gives himself, in order to assign from there a particular motion to each of the other systems, since there is no absolute motion. He can choose any one of the systems in his universe; he can, moreover, change systems at any moment; but he is obliged to be in one of them at a particular moment. As soon as he clearly realizes this, the reciprocity of acceleration becomes clear to him, for the system in which he installs himself is interchangeable with any other system he is considering, whatever its motion, provided this system is conceived in itself and not in the perspective representation in which he provisionally sees it. Moreover, real time is what the physicist perceives and measures, what exists in the system in which he is installed; precisely because the moving system considered by him would be, when at rest, interchangeable with his at rest, our physicist would rediscover this same real time in the moving system being considered were he to project himself into it and, by that very fact, immobilize it, driving out then the phantasmal time which he had imagined in it and which, in actuality, could not be directly measured by anyone. But, precisely because he can imagine himself anywhere and shift at each instant, he likes to picture himself everywhere or nowhere. And, as all systems no longer then appear to him as referred to one among them—his own—all pass onto the same plane: in all of them at once he thus installs physicists who would be kept busy referring even though, alone motionless for the moment, our physicist is really the only referrer. This, at bottom, is what he is doing when he speaks of "systems of reference in motion." Each of these systems can undoubtedly *become* a system of reference for the physicist actually referred to, who will become a referrer, but it will then be motionless. As long as our physicist leaves it in motion, as long as he regards all these purely mental constructions simply as possible systems of reference, the only true system of reference is system S'' in which he himself has settled, in which he really computes time, and from which he then imagines those systems in motion

In short, there is nothing to change in the mathematical expression of the theory of relativity. But physics would render a service to philosophy by giving up certain ways of speaking which lead the philosopher into error, and which risk fooling the physicist himself regarding the metaphysical implications of his views. For example, we are told above that "if two identical, synchronized clocks are at the same spot in the system of reference, if we shift one very rapidly and then bring it back again next to the other at the end of time t (the time of the system), it will lag behind the other by $t - \int_0^t a\,dt$." In reality we should say that the moving clock exhibits this slowing at the precise instant at which it touches, still moving, the motionless system and *is about to re-enter it.* But, immediately upon re-entering, it points to the same time as the other (it goes without saying that the two instants are practically indistinguishable). For the slowed time of the moving system is only attributed time; this merely attributed time is the time indicated by a clock hand moving before the gaze of a merely imagined physicist; the clock before which this physicist is situated is therefore only a phantasmal clock, substituted for the real clock throughout its journey: from phantasmal it again turns into real the moment it is returned to the motionless system. It would, moreover, have remained real for a real observer during the trip. It would not have undergone any slow-

which are only potentially referrers. It is from the vantage of this system S'' that he really operates—even if he mentally sees himself everywhere or nowhere—when he portions out the universe into systems endowed with this or that motion. The motions are such and such only with respect to S''; there is motion or immobility only with respect to S''. If the physicist were really everywhere or nowhere, all these motions and immobilities would be absolute ones; we would have to say goodbye to the theory of relativity. Relativity theoreticians sometimes seem to forget this; nor, again, is it anything of which they need take notice as physicists since, as we have shown, the distinction between the real and possible vision, between the system of reference which is really adopted and the one merely imagined as such, necessarily disappears in the mathematical expression of the theory. But the philosopher must re-establish it once more.

ing. And that is precisely why it shows no slowing when it is again found to be a real clock upon arrival.

It follows that our remarks apply equally to clocks placed and displaced in a gravitational field.[5] According to the theory of relativity, what is gravitational force for an observer in the system becomes inertia, motion, acceleration, for an observer outside of it. In that case, when we are told of "modifications undergone by a clock in a gravitational field," is it a question of a real clock perceived in the gravitational field by a real observer? Obviously not; in the eyes of the latter, gravitation signifies force, not motion. But it is motion, and motion alone, that slows the course of time according to the theory of relativity, since this slowing can never be posited except as a consequence of the Lorentz formulae.[6] Hence, it is for the observer outside the field, mentally reconstructing the position of the clock hand but not seeing it, that the running of the clock is modified in the gravitational field. On the other hand, real time, indicated by the real clock, lived or capable of being lived, remains a time of unchanging rhythm; only a fictional time, which cannot be lived by anything or anyone, has its rhythm modified.

Let us take a simple case, selected by Einstein himself,[7] that of a gravitational field created by the rotation of a disk. On a plane S adopted as system of reference and by that very fact immobilized, we shall consider a motionless point 0. On this plane we shall set a perfectly flat disk whose center we shall have coincide with point 0, and we shall have the disk turn about a fixed axis perpendicular to the plane at this point. We

---

[5] Insofar as these clocks would be affected by the intensity of the field. We are now leaving aside the consideration, with which we have been occupied till now, of the slowing that overtakes the clock by the mere fact of its leaving and returning to its position.

[6] And since it depends solely, as we have shown (pp. 117ff.), upon the lengthening of the "light-line" for the person who, outside the system, imagines the "light-figure" distorted as the result of its motion.

[7] Albert Einstein, *La théorie de la relativité restreinte et generalisée*, pp. 68–70. Cf. Jean Becquerel, *Le principe de la relativité et la théorie de la gravitation*, pp. 134–136.

shall thus obtain a true gravitational field in the sense that an observer situated on the disk will note all the effects of a force pushing him away from the center or, as he will perhaps believe, drawing him toward the periphery. It matters little that these effects do not follow the same law as those of natural gravitation, that they increase in proportion to the distance from the center, etc.: everything essential in gravitation is present, since we have an influence which, emanating from the center, is exerted upon objects standing out clearly on the disk, without taking into account the substance interposed, and produces on all things, whatever their nature or structure, an effect that depends only upon their mass and distance. Now, what was gravitation for the observer when he inhabited the disk, and thus immobilized it into a system of reference, will become an effect of rotational, that is, accelerated, motion when he betakes himself to point 0 of system S with which the center of the disk coincides, and when he gives this system, as we ourselves do, the status of a system of reference. If he pictures clocks located at various distances from the center of the disk's surface and considers them for a time short enough for their circular motion to be likened to a uniform translation, he will, of course, believe that they cannot run synchronously, since their respective speeds are at that moment proportional to the distance separating them from the center: the Lorentz equations do indeed indicate that time slows down when speed increases. But what is this time which slows down? What are these nonsynchronous clocks? Are we dealing with the real time, with the real clocks perceived a moment ago by the real observer situated in what seemed to him to be a gravitational field? Obviously not. We are dealing with clocks that are pictured in motion, and they can be pictured in motion only in the mind of an observer considered motionless in his turn, that is, outside the system.

One sees at what point the philosopher can be misled by a manner of expression that has become current in the theory of relativity. We are told that a physicist, setting out from point 0 with a clock and walking with it across the disk, would perceive, once he has returned to the center, that it is now slower than the clock, synchronized beforehand, which was left at point 0. But the clock that begins to slow down immediately upon setting out from point 0 is a clock which, from that moment on, has become phantasmal, being no longer the real clock of the real physicist—the latter has remained with his clock at point 0, detaching only a shadow of himself and of his clock onto the disk envisaged as moving (or else, each point of the disk, upon which he will actually settle, becoming, for that reason, motionless; his clock, having remained real, will everywhere be motionless and everywhere work the same way). Wherever you put the real physicist, he will bring immobility with him; and every point on the disk where the real physicist sits is a point from which the observed effect will have to be interpreted no longer in terms of inertia, but of gravitation; the latter, as gravitation, changes nothing in the rhythm of time or in the running of the clocks; it does so only when it is construed as motion by a physicist for whom the clocks and times of the system, where he no longer is,[8] have become mere mental views. Let us therefore say that if we keep our real physicist at 0, his clock, after having traveled toward the periphery of the disk, will return to 0 just as it was, running as before, not having slowed down. The theory of relativity here simply requires that there be a slowing down at the precise instant it rejoins 0. But at that precise instant it is again, as before at the precise instant of leaving the system, phantasmal.

We fall, moreover, into an analogous error, admissible in the physicist, dangerous for the philosopher, when we say that, in a system such as the turning disk, "it is not possible to define time by means of clocks motionless with respect to the system." Is it true that the disk constitutes *a* system? It is a

---

[8] When we say that the physicist is no longer in the system, we mean, of course, that he does not wish to be in it any longer. He may really live in the system; but he mentally projects himself outside it and adopts another as system of reference the moment he explains gravitation in terms of motion.

system if we imagine it motionless; but we are then placing the real physicist upon it; and at any point on the disk where we have the real physicist with his real clock, there is, as we just saw, the same time. Time undergoes different slowings at different points on the disk; and clocks situated at these points cease to be synchronous, only in the imagination of the physicist who no longer adopts the disk and for whom the disk, being thus again found in motion, again comes under the Lorentz equations. But, in that case, the disk no longer constitutes a single system; it breaks up into an infinite number of separate systems. Let us actually track one of its radii, considering the points at which this radius intersects the inside circumferences, infinite in number, which are concentric with that of the disk. These points are impelled at the same instant by different tangential speeds, the greater the speed, the farther from point 0: they therefore belong to different systems for the motionless observer at 0, who applies the Lorentz formulae; while a dt time elapses at 0, it is a slowed adt time that our observer will have to attribute to any one of these moving points, a depending, again, upon the speed of the mobile and, consequently, upon its distance from the center. Hence, contrary to what is said, the "turning" field has a perfectly definable time when it constitutes a system, for then, bearing the physicist, it does not "turn"; this time is the real time to which all the system's real and therefore synchronous clocks actually point. It ceases to have a definable time only when it "turns," the physicist having transported himself to the motionless point 0. But, in that case, it is no longer one system, but an infinity of systems; and we shall naturally find on them an infinity of times, all fictional, into which real time will have been pulverized, or, rather, evaporated.

To sum up, we have a choice of one of two things. Either the disk is considered as turning and gravitation is there resolved into inertia: we are then viewing it from the outside; the living, conscious physicist does not dwell on it; the times that unwind on it are only conceived times; there will, of course, be an infinity of them; the disk will, moreover, not constitute a system or object, it will be the name we give to a collectivity; we shall obtain, for the application of the Lorentz formulae, as many separate systems as there are physical points impelled by different speeds. Or else, this same turning disk is considered motionless: its inertia of a moment ago becomes gravitation; the real physicist lives there; it really is a single system; the time we find on it is real, lived time. But, in that case, we find the same time on it everywhere.

The Library of Liberal Arts